Glad you've kept up with the modelling, Ted

---⊙---

Modern Aeromodelling

---⊙---

Your old chum,
Ron

GW00360629

by the same author

*

AEROMODELLER ANNUAL

FLYING SCALE MODELS

MODEL AERO ENGINE ENCYCLOPAEDIA

CONTROL LINE MANUAL

(*Published by Model and Allied Publications Ltd*)

R. G. MOULTON

Modern Aeromodelling

WITH LINE ILLUSTRATIONS BY

R. J. SILVESTER

FABER AND FABER
3 Queen Square
London

First Published in 1963
by Faber and Faber Limited
3 Queen Square London WC1
Second edition 1968
Reprinted 1969
Revised edition 1974
Printed in Great Britain by
Whitstable Litho, Whitstable, Kent

ISBN   0   571   04852   8

The author would like to record the co-operation
of Model and Allied Publications Ltd
publishers of *Aeromodeller*, for use of
photographs and technical data

Contents

5

CONTENTS

6

Illustrations

PHOTOGRAPHS

ILLUSTRATIONS
DIAGRAMS

ILLUSTRATIONS

IMPERIAL ENGLISH MEASURE EQUIVALENTS OF METRIC FIGURES IN COMMON USE FOR AEROMODELLING REGULATIONS

MEASURES OF LENGTH OR THICKNESS:

0,30 mm = 0·0118 ins	650 mm = 25·590 ins	40 m = 131 ft. 2· 8 ins
6 mm = 0·236 ins	750 mm = 29·527 ins	45 m = 147 ft. 7·65 ins
10 mm = 0·394 ins	1000 mm = 39·370 ins	50 m = 164 ft. 0· 5 ins
14 mm = 0·551 ins	1250 mm = 49·213 ins	100 m = 328 ft, 1· 0 ins
19 mm = 0·748 ins	2,5 m = 98·426 ins	150 m = 492 ft. 1· 5 ins
25 mm = 0·984 ins	3 m = 9 ft. 10·11 ins	300 m = 984 ft. 3· 0 ins
38 mm = 1·496 ins	8 m = 26 ft. 2·96 ins	400 m = 1312 ft. 4· 0 ins
40 mm = 1·574 ins	10 m = 32 ft. 9· 7 ins	50km = 31 miles 364 ft. 3·84 ins
50 mm = 1·969 ins	15 m = 49 ft. 2·55 ins	500km = 310 miles 3,643 ft. 2·40 ins
68 mm = 2·677 ins	15,92 m = 52 ft. 2·77 ins	
85 mm = 3·346 ins	19, 6 m = 64 ft. 3·65 ins	
175 mm = 6·889 ins	19, 9 m = 65 ft. 3·46 ins	
	21, 5 m = 70 ft. 5·46 ins	
	30 m = 98 ft. 5·10 ins	

MEASURES OF WEIGHT:

1 gram = 0·0353 oz.	300 g = 10·581 oz.	1 kg = 35·274 ozs.
40 g = 1·410 oz.	410 g = 14·461 oz.	2 kg = 70·544 ozs.
200 g = 7·054 oz.	500 g = 17·635 oz.	2·2 kg = 77·603 ozs.
230 g = 8·112 oz.	700 g = 24·689 oz.	3 kg = 105·824 ozs.
		5 kg = 11 lbs. 0·368 ozs.

SQUARE MEASURES:

2,5 dm^2 = 38·75 sq. ins.	19 dm^2 = 294·50 sq. ins	39 dm^2 = 60·450 sq. ins.
12,0 dm^2 = 186·00 sq. ins.	32 dm^2 = 496·00 sq. ins	45 dm^2 = 697·50 sq. ins.
17,0 dm^2 = 263·50 sq. ins.	34 dm^2 = 527·00 sq. ins	300 dm^2 = 4650·00 sq. ins.
		150 dm^2 = 2325·00 sq. ins.

CUBIC MEASURES

2,5 cm^3 = 0·153 cu. ins	6,6 cm^3 = 0·403 cu. ins
5 cm^3 = 0·305 cu. ins	10 cm^3 = 0·610 cu. ins

MEASURE OF AREA LOADING:

12g/dm^2 = 3·95 oz./sq. ft.	50g/dm^2 = 16·38 oz./sq. ft.	100g/dm^2 = 32·76 oz./sq. ft.
20g/dm^2 = 6·55 oz./sq. ft.	75g/dm^2 = 24·57 oz./sq. ft.	150g/dm^2 = 49·14 oz./sq. ft.

SPEED:

4m/sec = 8·947 mph
12m/sec = 26·843 mph

POWER LOADING:

300 g/cm^3 = 10·581 oz./cm^3
2 dm^2/cm^3 = 31 sq. in./cm^3

Introduction

Little more than a century ago, Penaud made successful flights with what has since been acknowledged to be the very first model aeroplane. This preceded Orville and Wilbur Wright's great flight at Kitty Hawk by more than thirty-three years, yet the configuration of the French model would be acceptable today for an interesting experimental flying machine.

From that adventurous first step, progress was slow and delayed with disappointment. Not until the full-size pioneers created a national interest in aviation, did this hobby of making model aeroplanes become a popular and rewarding pastime.

In the last thirty years, aeromodelling has kept pace with the rapid developments of the aircraft industry by introduction of its own specialist materials and techniques. Indeed, the aircraft industry leans heavily on the hobby as a means of experiment in reduced scale, and also as a recruiting source for those with a valued enthusiasm for aviation. We have progressed from cane, spruce and oiled silk covering to moulded plastics and butyrates.

There are so many sides to the hobby, and the standards of performance in the specialist classes of contest model have become so high, that the relative novice is bewildered and seeks guidance as to which avenue he might best explore.

It is hoped that this volume will serve to explain the techniques of this fascinating hobby and illustrate the enormous benefits to be enjoyed. One does not have to be a skilled craftsman, or to possess an elaborate workshop. The very essence of the pastime is its simplicity, and the usual building area is the kitchen table. It offers an exercise in patience of inestimable value to the younger person; the outdoor activity in flying one's own creation rewards with a healthy

11

INTRODUCTION

appreciation of the open air and countryside, while family interest fosters with parent participation. Make no mistake—it's a grand hobby, and if you are new to it, then perhaps what follows will help to encourage further your interest and enjoyment.

CHAPTER 1

───────────────◎───────────────

Types of Flying Model

───────────────◎───────────────

Simplest of the flying models is the small glider made from balsa wood sheet and destined for catapult launch or the javelin style hurl of a more vigorous modeller. Most complex of models is the radio controlled type with multiple engines and many channels of selective control working numerous operations. Between the two, representing as they do a few moments' effort at the expense of a few pence and countless hours of design study, fabrication and electronic installation at inestimable cost, we find a dozen or more 'classes' of model to build and fly.

Broadly speaking, we have three categories, each subdivided into various classifications. They are: *Free-flight, Control-line* and *Radio controlled.* Taking the **Free-flight** category first, we have the following classes: *Glider* (hand-launched, cable-launched* or special type for slope soaring). *Power driven* (Sport flier or outright contest duration* type). *Rubber driven* (Sport flier or outright contest duration* type). *Indoor flier* (Microfilm* or tissue covered). *Scale* (Glider, power-driven or rubber-driven). There are also many *unorthodox* applications in the free-flight category, for example, the delta, canard, ornithopter and helicopter configurations.

In **Control-line**, where models are tethered by lines to a pilot's handle and are thus remote controlled throughout the flight, we have the following classes: *Aerobatic.* Speed.* Combat. Team racer** (in several distinct classifications). *Sport flier. Scale.* Unorthodox.* Also there are many ready-to-fly-plastics as they are known which can be purchased in finished condition for amusement flying.

Radio control is perhaps the aim of all model enthusiasts. The classes are: *Sport flier* (with any number of operating controls). *Contest type* (single control on rudder only, intermediate type with a

13

single channel operating two or more controls and multi channel*
with at time of writing, up to six controls through twelve channels).
Scale. *Pylon racer*. *Combat*.

This variety of flying models could be even further emphasized with
extra subdivision of the classes; but for the moment it is sufficient to
know the salient differences between types and not to confuse with
information that will follow in other chapters.

WORLD CHAMPIONSHIPS

What must be understood at this stage is that only those classifications which are marked with an asterisk * are recognized for World
Championships. These take place during August or September each
year, the radio control and control-line events alternating with the
free-flight classes so that, for example, 1973 was the year for the
World Championships in free flight, held in Austria, and radio
control in Italy; in 1974 the control-line Championships took place
in Czechoslovakia, with Indoor and Scale events in the U.S.A.

National teams are selected through strict eliminating contests and
consist of three modellers plus the team manager. As many as thirty
nations will send a team to the free flight championships, and sometimes the participants are obliged to encircle the world when travelling to and from the event, as for example the Japanese, New Zealand
and Australian competitors who have appeared in person at championships held in Great Britain. Finance does not always permit
this, and here the international camaraderie of aeromodelling comes
to the fore. Proxy fliers are appointed in the host country to fly
models which are despatched with ample instruction and accessories.
It is by no means uncommon for a proxy-flown model to place very
high in the results, since host nations are usually those with particular
enthusiasm for a class and have many expert fliers at their disposal
who have proven their capability in the eliminators for team selection.

These World Championship classes are run to a Sporting Code
issued by the Fédération Aéronautique Internationale (F.A.I.) and
all models are required to meet a stringent specification. As may well
be expected, the classes demand a high standard of workmanship and
technique, and for this reason alone, only a small proportion of
aeromodelling enthusiasts specialize in F.A.I. types.

This is not to say that the novice has no chance to progress to the
standard needed for international competition. The class specifi-

14

cations are specially created so that consistent skill in technique over the number of flights required is the key factor. Levelling devices such as the application of a standard fuel rule for speed models, and maximum recognized duration (for the first five flights) of three minutes in free flight, serve to match the established experts with relative newcomers so that consistency in achievement provides the individual and team winners.

National teams can only be sent under the auspices of the recognized aero club, in the case of Great Britain this being the Royal Aero Club, to which the Society of Model Aeronautical Engineers (S.M.A.E.) is affiliated as the body delegated to administer the hobby of aeromodelling.

Similarly, the S.M.A.E. has and will be responsible for the organization of World Championships. The 1972 radio-control Pylon Race contest was held at Cranfield to support the indoor model Championships at Royal Air Force Station, Cardington. In 1970 the World Scale Model Championships were held at Cranfield. All of which serves to illustrate the active part played by this country in International aeromodelling. Models have represented Great Britain at every World Championship yet held, gaining many first places in the process.

It is as well to understand a little of this World Championship modelling before we detail the other types. Although only a small percentage of modellers actually engage in these specialized events, the very fact that they are used to determine Champions creates an interest among the great majority, who look upon the team place winners with a certain amount of awe and admiration. The classic event is that of rubber-driven duration. It is the oldest-established International contest, and by virtue of its original sponsor who donated the magnificent trophy (won in 1973 by J. Löffler, East Germany, at the contest in Austria) is known as the 'Wakefield'.

Whilst there may be but less than a hundred 'Wakefield' specialists willing to enter the team trials for 1974/5 in Great Britain, there will certainly be many times that number of enthusiasts who are keenly interested in following the progress of the contest, many of them actually flying this type of model but with a little less confidence in ability than is needed for the trials.

TYPES OF FLYING MODEL

Choosing Your Type

We find people from all walks of life on the model flying field. There are no distinctions, and the fellowship of the local club is something to really appreciate. Helpful hints for the beginner, loan of equipment, test flying of a new project are in the normal programme for any club meeting.

The only division comes in our human nature. We are all 'typed'. Some like to tinker with the complex, others want quick results and demand simplicity in extreme.

This is where one must follow personal instincts in making an initial selection of the type of model one wishes to construct. Doctors prefer detailed control-line models. Engineers like speed and team racers. Draughtsmen take up the free flight duration classes. Research technicians adopt radio control. These are generalizations of surprising accuracy.

It takes the utmost in perseverance to achieve flights of more than a half-hour with a microfilm covered indoor model and it requires only common sense and interest to assemble a prefabricated kit for a sport free-flight model which will fly for as long as the small two-stroke engine in the nose is permitted to run. Design development in commercial kits and plans is such that any novice can be guaranteed some stage of success provided the general construction is to a reasonable standard. Thus in a sport design, the limitation is that of engine run. The model will climb for as long as the engine is permitted to run and that means for the time it takes to consume its fuel or until an automatic timer stops the engine fuel supply from the tank.

Free Flight

So if one has an inclination for the free-flying model (and enough local space over which to exercise the creation) then the type selected depends upon one's personal whims.

However, it is strongly advised that a simple glider be selected as a first effort.

Divorced from the complication of an engine or rubber motor, the glider provides a simple exercise in construction and a most valuable instruction in how to 'trim' a model for flight. Gliders can be elementary 'chuck' type, trimmed only by moving the centre of gravity or

16

balance point by adding or taking away weight from the extreme nose, or they can be larger, up to 10-ft. wingspan designs which are launched kite fashion by towing into the air on a line.

The towline glider very often remains the first and last love of an aeromodeller for its graceful silent flight. With occasional exciting flights of long duration in thermal upcurrents, it is most rewarding for so little comparative effort. It teaches one the need for adjustment to wing and tail surfaces, offers a greater degree of tolerance for sloppiness in structure and inferior covering smoothness, and above all, is by far the least expensive of all the free-flight classes.

The rubber-driven model adds that extra fascination of power to what is otherwise a glider. Modern manufacturing methods with plastic moulding have allowed much of the hard work in producing the propeller to disappear and provided one limits the selection of the model type to that which will suit the plastic propellers on the market, then there is but a small difference between the glider and the rubber-driven model as a beginner's choice. Torque reaction on the airframe which is a consequence of the fast-turning propeller, adds a flight trim characteristic which must be recognized, and the flier soon learns the use of side and downthrust to compensate the less desirable torque reactions. The duration of the rubber motor will vary from 20 to 50 sec. according to the type of propeller and size of model, and this, starting with a burst of high power and tapering off towards the end until the propeller 'freewheels', will allow a normal flight of approximately twice the power run duration. Thus a 20-sec. power run can be expected to result in a flight of 40 sec. from the time of launching to moment of landing.

A contest model will produce far better durations, climbing at greater rate to higher altitude and then gliding for longer. The improvement comes with a general lightening of the construction and in the more advanced design of wing and tail. Airfoils, or the actual profile of the wing and tail cross-section, are most important to some types of model, especially the contest rubber-driven class, as we shall explain later.

By far the most exacting of all models are the indoor fliers. They weigh but the merest fraction of an ounce—complete and ready to fly! They are so delicate in structure (down to $\frac{1}{64}$ in. × $\frac{1}{64}$ in. outlines to wing and tail) that the modeller can only walk at funereal pace with one of them for fear of breaking the parts. Flying speed is less than a very slow walking pace, the propeller revolves at about 40 revolutions per minute, and the World Record duration is not less than 45 minutes!

Whilst it must be acknowledged that this is truly an expert's class, and that the models meeting the above description require an airship hangar to realize their full capability, the indoor flier can be made in less refined manner, and to lower standards, to achieve good flights in the small clubroom, or home parlour. Flying around the pendant electric light fitting in the room centre can be fun, and with wing-spans of only 6 in., one can obtain amusing flights.

CONTROLLED FLIGHT

It is patently obvious that for a free-flight model, especially the engine-powered type, one must go to a large open space. Additionally there are many of us who do not favour the idea of chasing a model for any distance as it rapidly drifts downwind.

In consequence the line-controlled model enjoys greater popularity.

The model is attached to a controlling handle by means of inextensible lines, usually of piano wire. These connect to a bellcrank inside the model, and when tension is varied from line to line, the bellcrank actuates the elevator. Thus, when the 'pilot' moves the control handle up or down by wrist or arm action, the elevator responds and this in turn will cause the model to climb or dive. Since the control-line model will be rotating about the 'pilot' in the centre of the circuit, the elevator action can be used to produce any form of flight path permitted with the periphery of the hemisphere created by the radius of action, and so we get loops, figures of eight, cloverleaf and hourglass figures with the fully aerobatic types.

Speed control-line models are not intended to do anything other than straight around the circuit flights at level altitude and fastest possible speed. They are timed by stopwatch over a number of laps equal to a kilometre or a half-mile and in order to prevent the 'pilot' cheating by application of manual assistance through whipping, the operator's wrist has to be engaged with a central pylon. Speeds of up to 180 miles per hour are possible, this with pulse jet and 10 c.c. engine power, while even the smallest class with only 0·8 c.c. engine capacity can return a Championship speed of 100-plus m.p.h.

These models are as close to model engineering as others are to kitchen table aeromodelling. The fuselage is usually a special light

18

alloy casting in its base, and the engine/tank/propeller combination, to say nothing of the fuel blend in many cases, is a derivative of long experiment. Engines are highly modified, and the flying techniques employ a single line-control known as 'Monoline' in order to reduce the line drag. This is a highly specialized class on the whole, the exception being the World Championship class for those models with engines up to 2·5 c.c., where fuel must be to a standard formula, and the model specification places everyone on a common starting base.

Combat is exactly what the name suggests. We take two aerobatic models, fly them in the same circuit on the same length of line, and attach a streamer to each. The object is to clip the opponent's streamer as many times as possible to accumulate a high points score within the five-minute 'joust' time. Against this score is a penalty system giving points loss for time on the ground.

As may well be imagined, this is an exciting class, and surprisingly it is not in any way as difficult as first imagined. One needs an aggressive outlook and a will to win, and perhaps it is significant of modern times that the Combat type of model enjoys greater popularity (as a single class) than any other. As many as 150 entrants will appear at a Rally for 'jousts' on a knock-out basis.

Less destructive but by no means less exciting is Team Racing. This is the actual racing of semi-scale models, up to as many as four at a time in the common circuit. Each model has a tank and engine of restricted capacity. The course is a set length of 5 kilometres or miles for the racing heats, then the fastest team of pilot and mechanic qualify for semi-finals and a grand final of double distance. The mechanic is the key man. He is usually the owner/entrant and it is his efficiency in the two or three pit stops which can win or lose a race. Ten miles has been covered in little over 6 min. including pit stops, and with close passing of the fast racers, there is a thrill on every lap.

So keen are the modellers to enjoy the excitement of team racing, that a less refined class has been derived, known as 'Rat Racing'. Here we do not heed any specification or tank restriction. Models have to make a pit stop every 70 laps or so and apart from that, the regulations are practically nonexistent. It is racing for all kinds of control-line model, with the aerobatic and combat types mixed among genuine team racers (real speedsters have no undercarriages and so cannot comply with the pit stop requirement).

19

TYPES OF FLYING MODEL

There are also the plastic ready-to-fly models which come complete with small engine, control handle and lines. Semi-scale in appearance and comparatively heavy for the power, these models have a limited capability but at the same time do serve as safe tutors for the absolute novices. By no stretch of the imagination can it be accepted that a counter-purchased ready-to-fly represents true aeromodelling, but at least it *is* a start!

RADIO-CONTROLLED FLIGHT

Rounding up the classes in the hobby we come to the apex with radio control. This is so large a subject, with possibilities as yet not fully fathomed, that a simple résumé is impossible.

Controls are just as on full-size light aircraft, and in the case of the elementary single-channel equipment, where only one control is operated, it is the rudder which is controlled. In multi-channel, the equipment varies from derivation of principles that are over 50 years old to a fully proportional joystick control that is a product of the '70s. In all cases, the object of the exercise is to have the model under full control *all* of the time and to bring it back to one's feet safe and sound. Accidents happen, and a strong wind has often blown away a rudder-only-controlled model despite full equipment reliability; but in the main we can say that latest radio-control gear does enable the modeller to achieve all he wants. Such progress does not come cheaply, and any model with an 8 c.c. engine, pneumatic wheels, ten-channel receiver and five control servos will be worth well over one hundred pounds by the time it is airborne.

These are the fully aerobatic designs. They can fully emulate the real aeroplane in loops, figures of eight, stalls, touch and go landings and some even have retractable undercarriages. If superhets are used, then spot frequency channels permit five or six models to be flown at once—sometimes in combat with towed streamers. A special Post Office licence is needed, at a cost of only £1 for five years, and this allows use of the transmitter within a set frequency band. Present-day equipment is reliable and calls for little attention in tuning. It makes use of the very latest Integrated Circuit, or 'I.C.' chips as they are known, and eliminates the old risks of many small components, each with a joint. It employs the ingenious nickel-cadmium cell accumulators. These can be re-charged and the modern transistor enables the boffins to create power amplifiers, so that for a trans-

20

mitter we use only three ni-cad cells of 3·6 volt total, and amplify this to much higher voltage. Similarly, the mechanical relay is replaced by a switching transistor. We also have safety circuits which prevent the receiver from working unless the right transmitter is being operated, again using the modern transistor.

The blend of electronics and aeromodelling is very much for the advanced man and one with adequate funds. However, the rewards are proportional to the investment and in the event of mishap, it is the airframe and not the radio gear which suffers. The capable modeller can make his own set from plans or a kit of parts and get adequate local field flying fun provided he is satisfied with single control, and this should not cost much more than ten pounds over the price of the model and engine.

Kits and plans are the ideal means of introduction to the hobby. To attempt a self-design without experience is foolhardy when manufacturers and publishers market their wares at such low rates. Plans are complete in themselves, and the range carried by the *Aeromodeller Plans Service* includes more than a thousand different designs of all types.

On the other hand, one may prefer to have everything complete in one kit box, and here the many prefabricated outfits, with wood die-stamped and many shaped parts are time and patience saving. The local model shop will have a display and can offer direct advice on available stock.

AEROMODELLING IN INDUSTRY

Thus far we have dealt with aeromodelling as a hobby. It is also a profession in the aircraft industry. All aircraft start life nowadays as windtunnel or visual display models and all the problems in design are solved by study of the project in miniature. This is outside the sphere of a lad flying for fun in the local park; but his problems are so close to those of many real aircraft designers, that the cause of an aviation disaster is frequently detected by study of model behaviour. Spin recovery tests are made with radio-equipped models dropped from captive balloon or helicopter, and these relatively inexpensive test models have saved many lives and aircraft.

────────◎────────

CHAPTER 2

Materials and Tools

────────◎────────

During the early '20s, when the spruce framed, oiled silk covered model was in vogue, the main bugbear which retarded performance was availability (or lack of it) of the flat strip rubber. Modellers had resolved their structural difficulties—or so they thought.

Then word came through from the U.S.A. where a remarkable 'new' discovery had been made in the shape of balsa wood. Averaging only one-third of the weight of spruce, bass or pine, and offering the same required strength for cross-section, balsa opened up an entirely different interest in aeromodelling and created a hobby which was to be known as 'razor-blade carpentry'.

The wood originates in the damp forests of high altitude Ecuador. Natives use it for rafts, in fact the name has its origin as the word for a raft. On these rafts, they float banana crops to the seaports. Following the very considerable demand for balsa during World War II, the question of whether the raft is more valuable than its burden has no doubt helped to aid the lot of the Ecuador native. Certainly, the balsa industry has enlarged tremendously in post-war years, and it is far from the case of having to take what the native thought good enough for a raft.

Balsa is selected into weight grades, sizes of log, and for staining. Since a tree matures in as little as eight years, and the pithy nature of the timber in specially wet areas may be stained by minerals in the soil, buyers at the cutting mills can afford to be selective so that the modeller can still purchase his pristine sheet of $\frac{1}{32}$ in. × 3 in. × 36 in. over on the other side of the world.

During the war, attempts were made to establish the tree in the West Indies, India, Ceylon and other parts. None proved to be as satisfactory a source as the random harvest from Ecuadorian forests. Thus, from this small area, all of the aeromodellers in the world, regardless of politics, obtain their principal material for construction.

The timber is sold in block, sheet, strip or moulded shape form. Grades can vary from heavy and hard (18 lb./cubic foot) to soft and light (5 lb./cubic foot) and the sheets are cut in all manner of grain directions so that one can select stock for particular purposes (Fig. 1).

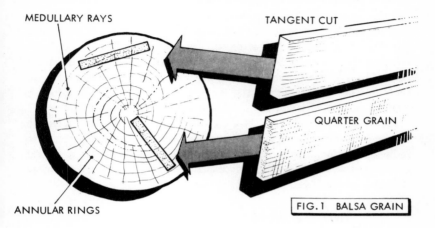

MEDULLARY RAYS

TANGENT CUT

QUARTER GRAIN

ANNULAR RINGS

FIG. 1 BALSA GRAIN

'Quarter grain' **Sheet** has a speckled finish and is easily recognized. It resists bending, and is prone to split if one attempts to force a bend. It has been cut in a direction that was radial from the centre of the log so that all the medullary rays (which also radiate from the centre of the log) run across the sheet surface. This, coupled with the regularly spaced annular rings which form a distinctly different pattern of grain, makes 'quarter grain' quite the prettiest of balsa cuts.

The newcomer should avoid it for any component likely to be bent or in need of flexibility. Use it for ribs, trailing edges, sheet tailplanes where its natural resistance to warping is a considerable advantage. If when buying a stock of balsa one discovers that a few sheets have this quarter grain, it is advisable to save them specifically for rigid parts, and to purchase replacement tangent-cut sheets. This tangent-cut has only one grain appearance. There are irregular and fairly deep grain lines. If the sheet is dampened on one side only it will curve in the direction of the dampness as it dries. If cellulose is applied to one side only, the sheet will curve and remain set. This way we can make a single surface wing with elementary airfoil curve.

23

MATERIALS AND TOOLS

Tangent-cut sheet will vary in hardness from side to side or end to end. This is because it has been 'selected out' at cutting stage by the mill to be left for sheet cuts as distinct from the strip and moulded shapes.

Strip is available down to $\frac{1}{16}$ in. × $\frac{1}{16}$ in. from $\frac{1}{2}$ in. × $\frac{1}{2}$ in. and in 36 in. lengths. Special orders can be obtained for metric sizes, 48 in. lengths or decimal fraction dimensions. All of it should be of equal hardness from end to end of the strip. The hardness will determine the flexibility, weight and strength. In consequence, it is better to select strips for their uniformity rather than for extreme hardness since if four strips of unequal flexibility are used for the longerons on the fuselage of a large model, then the fuselage will not adopt a natural symmetry when the sides are assembled together.

As a simple check, take the four strips and hold them in a bunch by the extreme ends. Wave them up and down (Fig. 2). If one strip indicates a reluctance to deflect as much as the other three, it should be rejected—even if in all other respects it appears to be of identical weight and hardness.

EQUAL FLEXING REQUIRED
IN STRIPS FOR LONGERONS

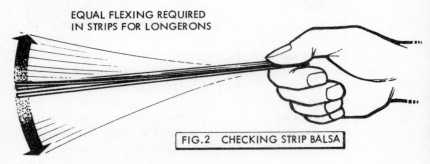

FIG.2   CHECKING STRIP BALSA

Moulded shapes are labour saving in that they offer leading and trailing edges ready to fit the airfoils in common use; but one should specially beware of unequal composition in trailing edges. Many a model has failed to rise to expectations because of wing warps, and the trailing edge is a key factor in this respect.

Weight is critical only for the competition enthusiast. The sport flier need have no qualms over use of heavier grade balsa in a model of up to 4 ft. wingspan. In a larger model, particularly in the case of radio-controlled types where there will be a payload to carry, the balsa should be selected.

This happy state is achieved through the high efficiency of model engines, propellers and rubber motors on sale today. The problem is more likely to be that of *over* rather than underpowering the model.

OTHER TIMBERS

While balsa remains the principal constituent of all home-constructed model aircraft, it is inferior in strength and surface finish for specific purposes. All model gliders of over 6 ft. wingspan should, for example, have the wingspars in **spruce**. The author uses spruce for the trailing edge as well. Similarly, in a large fuselage of built-up structure as distinct from one with sheet balsa strengthening, spruce is advised for the longerons. It is a valuable timber, three times as heavy as balsa; but offering a resistance to breakage that makes up for the weight penalty. **Obechi** is frequently quoted as a balsa substitute and should only be regarded as such.

On a scale model, not necessarily a flying type, one must achieve as smooth a surface as possible. **Lime** is the best known timber for closeness of grain and consistency of hardness. It is used for the majority of professionally-made display models, and one outstanding advantage is that it will shape down to a razor-like edge for scale trailing edges. For the flying model it offers no advantage whatsoever.

REEDS AND GRASSES

Bamboo and reed (of basket-making variety) have been used for undercarriage legs and wingtips for the whole period of the hobby. They have their uses as strengthening materials, and one well-known modeller persists in outlining every one of his designs with reed or bamboo let into the balsa leading and trailing edges plus tips. He claims, justifiably, that this outer rim of hard yet very flexible protection renders his models almost crashproof. They are fast fliers, and one can verify the outstanding strength of his models (Fig. 3). However, the right grade of bamboo is very hard to locate. It is not the split cane type but is oval in section, up to $\frac{1}{4}$ in. across the width, and solid, not hollow.

Soviet countries experienced difficulty in obtaining balsa during the late '50s and introduced grasses for the structure of rubber-driven models. In appearance, the material is like small diameter drinking straws. It has to be used in a form of geodetic construction, and introduces untold problems of overlapping and half-lapping. Yet even when balsa supplies became easy to obtain for Soviet aero-modellers, they retained the grass framework for wings and tail-

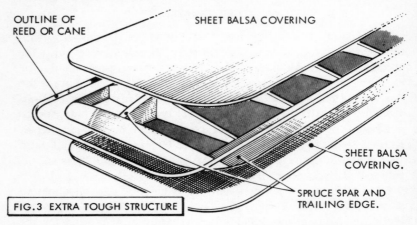

OUTLINE OF REED OR CANE

SHEET BALSA COVERING

SHEET BALSA COVERING.

SPRUCE SPAR AND TRAILING EDGE.

FIG.3 EXTRA TOUGH STRUCTURE

planes on contest designs. These grasses are not exploited outside the U.S.S.R., though no doubt there are many similar crops to be reaped in other lands. The effort in construction does not seem worthwhile so long as balsa supplies are maintained.

PLASTICS

For the home constructor there are three forms of plastics which are exploited successfully (Fig. 4). Most commonplace is **acetate** sheet for transparent cockpit mouldings. This is a thermoplastic which will adopt intricate curves when heated in front of a source such as an electric fire of 3 kilowatts. One has to prepare a mould and have the acetate pinned in place over a frame. When the acetate is very hot and has given off a great deal of its water content in vapour, it is floppy and can be forced over the mould, but since it cools very quickly, the action must be immediate. Cockpit canopies, wheel spats, engine cowlings, wingtips are but a few possibilities.

Royalite is the trade name for another thermoplastic marketed by the North British Rubber Co. and which is to be seen in facias of modern cars and for decorative mouldings in general use. It requires an oven for heat moulding, so unless you are a baker or brick maker, it is unlikely that the material has practical possibilities for you. It is very easily worked, and a model moulded in Royalite is virtually crash-proof.

Expanded polystyrene is the third usable plastic. The material comes in granulated form and these expand when heated. Steam heat is normally applied in manufacturing processes. One can make a

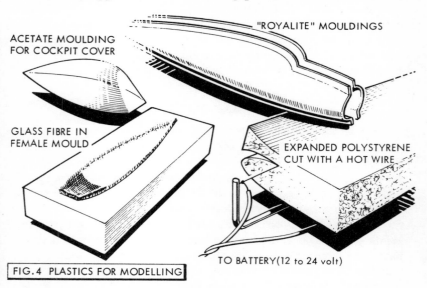

ACETATE MOULDING
FOR COCKPIT COVER

"ROYALITE" MOULDINGS

GLASS FIBRE IN
FEMALE MOULD

EXPANDED POLYSTYRENE
CUT WITH A HOT WIRE

TO BATTERY(12 to 24 volt)

FIG.4 PLASTICS FOR MODELLING

fuselage, then pack it out with the expanded polystyrene, or ideally, make a mould and expand the granules inside to produce the component. Unfortunately, the plastic must be protected from model engine fuels which are powerful solvents, and cellulose finishes, so the best and in fact most practical application is to purchase the expanded polystyrene in sheet form. These are sold by builders' merchants for loft insulation and come in a range of thicknesses. The material can be cut easily with a hot wire and in order to prepare a wing, all one has to do is to shape the planform roughly, set up two stiff templates for the cross section at each end of the cutting jig, and pass the hot-wire cutter over the edges of these templates, with the plastic in between. A wing is shaped by this method in a fraction of normal construction time and for both protection and strength, the entire wing is surfaced with balsa sheet.

Wing rigidity is assured by the surface tension in much the same way as some full-size aircraft structures. In fact, expanded poly-

MATERIALS AND TOOLS

styrene is becoming increasingly popular for gliders and light aircraft.

It is used by many toy manufacturers who produce ready-to-fly models of 10–20 in. wingspan with expanded polystyrene surfaces strengthened along the leading edges with a layer of adhesive tape.

It is a material which simply clamours for experiment in the aeromodeller's hands and which will undoubtedly be subject to many constructional techniques as the more inventive modellers devise best ways and means to employ the lightweight material. It averages only 3 lb. per cubic foot and is thus lighter than balsa.

GLASS FIBRE

Considerably heavier than the plastics we have been discussing, but possessing extraordinary strength and hardness, glass fibre has its own special place in the hobby. It can be used for models in which the question of wing loading is less important. For example, speed and scale control-line types. Used for engine cowlings, wheel spats, even engine mounts in some cases and whole fuselages for team racers, glass fibre rewards with a durability at some weight penalty. Whole fuselages have been made for radio-control types, but these have been thinner shells, calling for internal structure as well.

In brief, the glass fibre comes as a mat, as a cloth of finer weave or in ribbon form. One mixes a special resin with a hardener, lines the mould with this liquid, places the glass fibre in the mould, pummels more resin through the glass fibre until all is impregnated—and simply leaves to set hard—as glass! It is *almost* as simple as that!

However, there *are* snags. A mould must be made, and it can be a male mould whereby the job is made over the top and so has a surface which is beautifully smooth on the interior yet needs lots of work to pretty up on the exterior. As an alternative, the female mould is hollow (it can be the result of a glass fibre 'take' off the male mould, or in plaster of Paris) and here the job is made on the inside so that a beautiful finish is obtained where needed, on the exterior. To achieve perfection, we can employ matching male and female moulds and get a superb surface on each of the sides.

In all cases the techniques are simple, and with practice one tends to become an addict, making all and sundry parts in glass fibre and utilizing it for household repairs to keep the family happy in spite of the pungent smell. The book by Warring, *The New Book of Glass*

28

Fibre, is a comprehensive guide which amply covers use for models, and also gives the necessary information on use of glass fibre for local reinforcement. This is an application which specially deserves more attention for larger models. The glass fibre is moulded over the top of existing construction. Thus the chin of a radio-controlled model, or the nose of a large glider is safeguarded against sudden contact with a rough landing area.

PLYWOOD

Extensively employed in Soviet countries where balsa is scarce, and naturally in the nation which produces the best quality plywood (Finland), thin 3-ply can be fretted for ribs and used in solid form for bulkheads. It is virtually the ideal, irreplaceable material for mounting engine bearer beams in a fuselage. It will accept all the glues, and provides a good joint. At the same time, it absorbs vibration to a degree and is oil resistant if the proper Aircraft Quality, grade 5V3, is bought. Commercial plywood which is made for general purpose work is not waterproof and not always strong enough for models. Always insist on resin-bonded waterproof ply.

In thickness of metric dimensions, it comes from the thinnest practical size at 0·3 mm., to be used for some sheeted areas on small gliders, to 1 mm. for facing ribs on a model with the detachable wings in two halves and also to make up 'boxes' to take thicker (6 mm.) plywood wing mounting 'tongues'. Thicker sizes are in fractions of an inch, and for our purposes, $\frac{5}{16}$ in. represents the thickest likely to be wanted and this would be for a main bulkhead. Sometimes an engine is actually mounted on plywood, and here one should be even more insistent that the Aircraft Quality is employed.

ADHESIVES

Model aircraft glues are peculiarly known as 'cements'. Nothing to do with concrete; but usually of a nitro-cellulose base with retarders, plasticizers and other additives to distinguish the brands. It is quick drying, the 'field repair' special type takes only 5 min. to set a joint, and 'normal' sets in 15 min. It is strong, and penetrates into the greedy end grain of balsa to the extent that a 'pre-cement' coat is to be advised for specifically stressed parts, so making an excellent cellulose key between parts. It is also a good gap filler and hides many a poor joint! Supplied in tubes, it is easy to apply, but tough on the fingers and clothes if one is careless. Special solvents are obtainable to remove cement smears from clothes and as for the hands, a good soak in the bath, with extra time taken to peel the cement skins off, is the author's remedy.

There are other types of adhesive which offer a better joint strength with the attendant delay in assembly through longer drying time, and these are non-cellulose.

Most popular of the non-tube glues is polyvinyl acetate, known as **P.V.A.** or 'white' glue. This dries within an hour, and almost disappears in the process. It has remarkable strength, soaks well into balsa grain and gives a joint that is superior to the 'cement' joint in every way except that it is *not* waterproof. For adding a large area of sheet wood over a wing or fuselage it is an ideal medium, permitting time to position and pin the work in place without prejudicing the joint with drying glue. The author uses P.V.A. almost exclusively for all types of model work and finds it advantageous from many points of view.

First and foremost the joint is neat. All smears disappear. Secondly it can be wiped off the hands or clothes before it is dry. Thirdly, it is a weight saver. Fourthly, it is very strong. Fifth, and very important, it does not warp.

That it requires a longer drying time (especially in cold winter weather) is perfectly acceptable. One can plan the building progress to take care of adequate drying period.

Cold water glues, where a powder is mixed with water as a 'one-shot' cement are also very strong indeed and are to be recommended where large plywood areas are to be joined. They are less suitable for balsa as the soakage into the timber can induce a warp. Here, the **Contact Adhesive** is recommended. On the other hand, if two large blocks of balsa are to be joined on their faces and so laminated for carving a fuselage, etc., then the cold water glue is ideal.

There are also the 'two-tube' Epoxy adhesives which will stick practically anything. **Araldite** is the original, and this is specially recommended since for the kitchen-table modeller with limited facilities, it is practically the equivalent of a welding plant. It can be used to adhere an exhaust stack made of aluminium on to the side of a model engine, or even to repair a broken engine casting. A development is the five-minute Epoxy by **Humbrol** or **Devcon** which sets very rapidly but requires a very clean joint for long-term use.

MATERIALS AND TOOLS

COVERING

It is a far cry from the first model aeroplane coverings of oiled silk to the ultra lightweight sheer skin of microfilm used on modern indoor models: but strangely enough, the modern radio-controlled model utilizes a return to tough silk surfacing with multiple coats of cellulose, topped by a varnish to take the place of old style finish.

Microfilm for the indoor models is virtually a chemical deposit in the form of a film, deposited as quick-drying liquid on to water. This is scooped off on a frame, and the film then self adhered to the balsa model. A simple formula for the film is: *2 oz. of standard clear dope, 1 oz of amyl acetate, 20 drops of castor oil (medicinal).* The technique is to pour from a spoon on to a large water area such as the bath and to move the spoon swiftly so that the film disperses rapidly. Since this is a specialist process, the reader is advised to request further information from the magazine *Aeromodeller* should he wish to engage in contest flying. For house-size models of 9 or 12 in. span, the formula above and the simple bath technique, with a wire hoop to scoop the film from the water is sufficient instruction for lots of fun in experiment.

Next lightest covering is **Japanese tissue.** This is a very thin, grained paper with a hard surface. It adheres to the balsa easily, shrinks without creasing if applied with care, and accepts clear dope for an admirable airtight surface.

Bamboo paper is heavier, and suitable for larger models. It can be obtained as a 'wet-strengthened' tissue, meaning that it will not break up if dampened and so it can be applied whilst wet to adopt peculiar curvatures.

Swedish tissue is more like the wrapping grade. It is cheaper, less strong and does not have the grain of the Eastern papers. It can be recognized by its 'hardness' which creates a strong 'rustle' as it is handled. Suitable for simple models and particularly those where a coat of dope is not desirable. Swedish tissue is passing out of favour as the softer grades of grained papers are being supplied from British and Eastern sources.

Fabric covering includes **silk** and all the man-made fibres except **Terylene** which though strong, is so unpredictable and certainly shrink resistant that it must be regarded as unsuitable. **Nylon** should be stretched as it is applied and liberally coated with shrinking dope,

31

but rarely gives trouble and is very strong. Silk should be applied while wet, then it will shrink as it dries and adopt the desired curves.

Other covering mediums have been 'discovered' from time to time: but few match the delightful colour range, lightness and toughness of **nylon-chiffon** which has been used by the author for many years and so far without as much as a single tear. Other models from his stable, covered in silk *and* with a superimposed layer of tissue to give extra strength and finish, have shattered on impact of a heavy landing!

Plastic sheet film, such as **Monokote** or **Solarfilm**, have taken over the radio control or other large-model covering needs (see p. 127). They are *not* as strong as fabrics, nor as durable, but they eliminate a lot of finishing and speed up construction.

FINISHES

Most aeromodellers like to put an extra effort into the finish and decoration of their models, in fact they often spend more time producing the shiniest, brightest surface than was actually taken to produce the airframe up to that stage.

We start with **sealers**. These fill the grain or surface undulations and go a long way to making wood have the smooth surface of metal. Sealers are a paste held in suspension in cellulose of non-shrinking variety. Coats can be applied in fast frequency of half-hour or so *but* when one has built up the desired depth of seal to fill the gaps, etc., it must be emphasized that the surface should be 'cut-back' or sanded right through to the original base level. This leaves all the hollows filled and obtains the smoothest surface. It removes excess Sanding Sealer which will otherwise 'craze' in due course of time and spoil the model. Never leave a large area of sealer unsanded, it is a certainty that this will result in a cracked or crazed effect within a couple of months. Unfortunately, the instructions on the bottle rarely convey this information.

Fillers are more drastic. They are a definite paste, and can be applied to fill larger grain indentations or to produce fillets and curves that are inconvenient to model in wood. Brummer filler and stopper is to be recommended and can best be applied with a piece of flexible celluloid, using this as a 'knife' to work the filler in position. Plastic wood too has its uses and the latest types do not have the earlier disadvantage of shrinkage upon drying out. Beware of weight in-

32

creases though, and if possible make the construction of the model such that fillers and similar additions are restricted to a minimum. The water-mixed cellulose fillers such as Polyfilla are very easy to use and give an excellent surface; but again—watch the weight increase!

Most 'dopes' are of cellulose base. The exceptions are the later type Butyrates which are fuel proof. Covering is shrunk with a clear dope through several coats until the desired toughness of surface and air sealing is obtained, then colour is applied as wanted. It is vitally important to check at the Model Shop that the colour will safely go over the clear. They should each be cellulose or Butyrate. Similarly, if the top colour is to be a 'Dayglo', the white base necessary to bring out the reflective qualities of the colour *must* be that paired by the same manufacturer for the purpose. Some weird results are likely otherwise!

There are also the **non-shrinking** clear cellulose lacquers. These are used as a varnish over the top of a final clear shrinking coat, and replacing colour. The shine and weatherproofing effects are well worthwhile. Such a finish would only be beneficial in a general free-flight type model where the colour of the covering material is sufficient decoration. It usually goes by the odd name of 'Banana Oil'. Of course, one need not apply a cellulose colour. It can be any of the four-hour drying **oil based varnishes** such as Valspar which is very popular, having good density of colour in one coat and being reasonably proof against fuel. It also has its own clear lacquer for a top finish of high gloss to go over the colour. While Valspar and the like can be applied **over** cellulose, one cannot apply cellulose over Valspar. Repairs should therefore always be with the same material.

There are other finishes in the course of development which will be available to the aeromodeller where manufacturers specialize in **acrylic** and **epoxy** 'plastics'; and while our American cousins have a lead on this there is likelihood of European sources opening up. Epoxy surfaces can be practically glass-like and have great advantages from many points of view.

For one thing, the gloss obtained eliminates the elbow grease needed to bring cellulose up to a high gloss. Waxed finishes, polished for countless hours, are a feature of the Concours d'Elégance at the model rallies, and while it will be a natural disappointment for the man who has taken such trouble in the past to see easy spray-on gloss finishes, the majority will readily appreciate its labour saving.

MISCELLANEOUS

The aeromodeller is a 'magpie'. He hoards bits and pieces 'in case they *might* be useful' and in this way his ingenuity pays many a dividend. Odd lengths of balsa offcut are never discarded and this scrapbox yields parts for many a model yet to come. In the same way, the miscellaneous accessories required for the hobby are handed down from model to model. Wheels, propellers, spinners, fuel tanks, bobbins for rubber-motor ends, ballraces, and general equipment are commercial items which often, once bought, are used repeatedly.

There are other basic materials which are expendable, namely the metals. **Piano Wire**—a general term for spring steel wire—is universal in its application for undercarriage legs, rubber-drive propeller shafts, etc. It is sold in 36-in. lengths and useful sizes range through even number Standard Wire Gauges (S.W.G.) from the thin 26 for very fine work to the ⅛-in. thick 10 gauge for strong undercarriages. Most common sizes are 20, 18, 16 and 14. The wire is best bent with the aid of a vice but care should be taken to see that acute right-angle bends do not strain the wire to the extent of splitting it. If a tight bend is needed with the larger gauge wire, use heat treatment to anneal the metal by putting the area to be bent in a gas flame until cherry red with heat. Allow to cool before bending. Some of the natural temper will be lost, but the bend will not have strained the wire surface.

Very fine gauge piano wire is used for the control-lines of a flying model and can be up to 75 ft. long. 30 S.W.G. is the size to employ for most models, though a heavy and fast type will call for 28 gauge. When making soldered joints with all piano wire, be sure to use an acid flux and preferably add a thin copper wire soldered binding to ensure adequate strength.

Other metals to be advised are **Aluminium** for small cranks, engine cowlings or trim tabs. This metal is easily adapted and will glue in place with Araldite. Where stiffer light metal is wanted, **Duralumin** is good. Many all-metal undercarriages are made in a single leaf spring of Dural. It is also ideal for cranks where a lot of wear is expected and particularly for engine bearer plates.

Copper tubing is to be recommended for the ventilator and feed tubes in a home-constructed fuel tank (which can be soldered up from a salvaged cocoa tin) since copper bends easily and the tube will not flatten at the bend. The extra weight over brass tube is negligible when the amount of material used is considered.

Fibre board is used for engine bearer plates, control cranks and in some cases for propeller blades. It should be the cloth-impacted type such as 'Paxolin' for best effect in most cases, but where in the use of a propeller blade, it becomes advisable to obtain a permanent curvature in the fibre, then the plain red fibre board is sufficient and holds shape.

Those, then are the *basic* materials used in modern aeromodelling. There remains a vast range of proprietary brands of accessories so that the modeller has opportunity to select, say a pair of wheels, or a propeller according to needs and the depth of his pocket. As with most things, it is largely a matter of obtaining value according to expenditure. Shoddy accessories do not last long in a hobby trade and all items stocked by reputable model shops can be accepted as reliable.

Tools

We have already referred to this hobby as **'razor-blade** carpentry'. The faithful shaving blade is the number one tool of the trade and is widely used in the single-edged, backed form for plain cutting and stripping, or as a split from the double-edged type (so that a sharp point is obtained) for cutting around curves. It pays to buy new blades. They are relatively cheap, and a finer cut is more easily made with a new, rather than a 'shaved' blade.

Modelling knife sets are also number-one items. Used for cutting through thicker material, and especially for carving, the author's favourites are those with various curved and pointed blades, and the whittling blade which is a couple of inches long.

Next on the list of priorities is a good pair of **pliers**. They should have hardened jaws and side cutters for nipping off thin wire. A square-nosed, a round-nosed and a pair of fine pointed pliers are the most useful triple set to have.

A **metal rule**, up to 24 in. long, and with dimensions in all inch fractions will serve both for design and stripping balsa. A **fretsaw** for plywood is most helpful, and for the quick cuts, the small Eclipse-type hacksaw is in constant work. A **vice** is not essential, but very handy, and the type to look for is the wide-jaw model with ability to accept large blocks, and to be clamped in all sorts of odd places ranging from an outdoor fence for a messy carving and sandpapering job to the workbench for cleaner indoor work.

A **hand drill** with range of twist drills from $\frac{1}{64}$ in. to $\frac{3}{8}$ in. (with $\frac{1}{4}$ in. shank to go in the chuck) and a special piece of 14 S.W.G. piano wire bent to fit the same chuck and to be used for winding up rubber motors, form part of all aeromodellers' tool kits (Fig. 5).

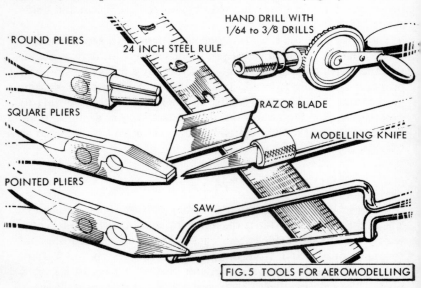

ROUND PLIERS

HAND DRILL WITH 1/64 to 3/8 DRILLS

24 INCH STEEL RULE

SQUARE PLIERS

RAZOR BLADE

MODELLING KNIFE

POINTED PLIERS

SAW

FIG. 5 TOOLS FOR AEROMODELLING

Pins, pins, pins by the hundred are the means of assembly. We pin the balsa framework over the plan, and when side frames are so made, join the parts together with more pins. Glass-headed spring steel pins are best. They will penetrate the hardest balsa and plywood. Domestic soft pins are not to be scorned, they are cheaper but have less repeat use after ends are accidentally bent.

Lastly and certainly the most essential of all the aeromodelling tools is the **building board.** These can be purchased, or the modeller may have the good fortune to possess a softwood-topped kitchen table. The determining factor is that the board shall be (*a*) flat and (*b*) soft enough to accept pins. Some people cover an otherwise unsuitable surface with thick linoleum or surfaced cork insulation. Whatever is used, the modeller must bear in mind that warps start at the building stage and if a board is twisted, then so will be the airframe.

Sight the board from end to end for squareness. If you find a suitable but rough plank of deal, get a local timber merchant to 'thickness' it. This will give a smooth, true surface.

CHAPTER 3

————————————◎————————————

Motive Power

————————————◎————————————

First of the successful flying models were hand-launched gliders. Then came the Penaud rubber-driven design. The elastic rubber motor has remained a most popular and economic power source and it is still the best introduction to all forms of power-driven flying model.

The rubber strip is flat, and sold in varying widths, the most common being $\frac{3}{16}$ in., $\frac{1}{4}$ in., 6 mm. and $\frac{1}{30}$ in., $\frac{1}{24}$ in. or 1 mm. thick. Round section rubber is used by Hungarian and U.S.S.R. aeromodellers but is not generally available.

The rubber strip is not specifically made for the purpose of driving model aircraft. It is a very small by-product of the large rubber product companies, notably Pirelli and Dunlop among others, and even the most searching enquiries have failed to elicit the actual reason for its manufacture! Suggestions range from special duty in mines to the binding of grape vines and grafting! Whatever the factual reasons, aeromodellers are thankful, though at the same time critical of the constantly fluctuating standards of manufacture. We get 'vintage' years just as with wine. The material also improves with maturing in storage. It should also be thoroughly examined and cleaned before first use if the model is a contest type.

Strange though it may seem, a microscope will reveal wood splinters and chemical crystals in profusion on a length of flat rubber strip!

If the large splinters are tweeked out with tweezers and the rubber washed with an ordinary soap solution (not detergent) it will last for a long time. The actual lifespan is dependent on the way the motor is treated in the first few winds. It has to be 'run in' and wound up in stages of 20 per cent turns so that on the fifth wind, the motor accepts full turns for peak performance, which it will hold many times. Some contest modellers have polythene bags for their rubber motors, each tagged and identified as to when used, the power flight characteristics, the duration and number of turns applied. This is the right way to go about contest work and by rotating the use of the motors with about six in service, it is possible to allow each motor adequate 'rest' period and to then check when its potential is on the wane.

Strands break but can be tied with a reef knot and additional thread binding (Fig. 6), and since there will be multiple strands in any motor

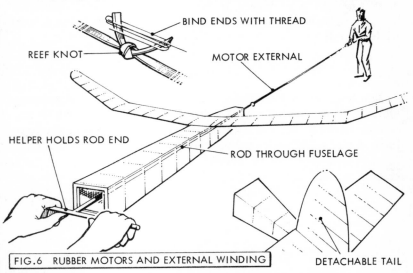

BIND ENDS WITH THREAD

REEF KNOT

MOTOR EXTERNAL

HELPER HOLDS ROD END

ROD THROUGH FUSELAGE

FIG.6   RUBBER MOTORS AND EXTERNAL WINDING

DETACHABLE TAIL

there is a reasonable safety margin. Complete failure *can* be disastrous as the collapse occurs almost always just as the very last turn is being applied on the winder. The thrashing of the broken motor can wreck a lightly constructed fuselage. In consequence, some aeromodellers have a system of winding up the motor *outside* the fuselage.

EXTERNAL WINDING

In order to slide a rubber motor clear of the fuselage and enable it to be fully wound externally, the fuselage must have detachable nose block, as is normal, and also a detachable tail unit. The tail is removed and the rear end of the rubber motor linked to a hook on a

39

long rod (steel or aluminium—it must be strong) the length of which is a few inches more than that for the fuselage. Once engaged with the rear end of the motor, the rod is used as a bearing over which the fuselage and wing assembly slides back. A helper must hold on to a T-shaped handle at the rod extremity to take the strain, and the rubber motor wound up.

When full turns have been applied, the fuselage is slid forward to meet the front end of the motor, and the rear end engaged with the rubber motor anchorage at the back of the fuselage. The tail unit is plugged in place, the nose block and propeller fitted and the flight made without risk of damage in the case of rubber motor failure.

It will be seen that the weakness of the system is that time is lost while reassembly of the nose and tail is going on.

Tube Winding

As a result of the time factor and also because there is the possibility of allowing the motor to contract to too short a length by the external method, the Croydon Club invented a tube-winding development (Fig. 7). This uses the long rod (and tube) but from the front

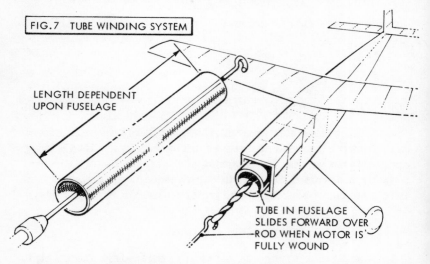

FIG.7 TUBE WINDING SYSTEM

LENGTH DEPENDENT UPON FUSELAGE

TUBE IN FUSELAGE SLIDES FORWARD OVER ROD WHEN MOTOR IS FULLY WOUND

end of the fuselage, eliminating the detachable rear fuselage. The winder is engaged with the end of the rod, over which is placed a tube of sufficient diameter to pass over the fully-wound motor. The rod is hooked on to the rubber motor, then the tube is slid over the rod, then over the rubber motor as it passes rearwards. As the tube reaches the anchorage for the rear end of the motor, it engages the crossbar at that point and so relieves the fuselage of *all* the winding strain.

We now have the tube *inside* the fuselage with the rubber motor stretched out through the front end and wound up on the end of the extension rod to full turns. Winding up is progressively relaxed so that from the fully stretched state, the motor is permitted to contract to the final length of the fuselage anchorage spacing, then the tube is slid forward, *out* of the fuselage and over the extension rod, leaving only the noseblock and propeller to fit in safety. The 'Croydon' system is further simplified by use of a winder with digital counter which eliminates all the concern of personally counting up the number of turns applied on the winding handle. By so relieving the operator of such mental strains, he is able to concentrate upon the actual technique of stretching and winding in order to get the best out of the power source. Some aeromodellers prefer to gradually withdraw the motor so that at about one-third full turns, it is stretched to its limit, then held there for the subsequent third of the turns, and brought back to fuselage length for the last third. Others stretch out as far as possible within a fifth of the total turns, and hold that stretch until literally pulled in by the tension of the motor. Whatever technique is used, the motor should not be wound up without knowledge of its theoretical limit.

The table gives the number of turns per inch of motor length. The measure of length is taken before the motor is made up into a tensioned skein which reduces the overall length to the distance between anchorages instead of being approximately one and a half times that distance.

Turns per inch

No. of strands	3/16 × 1/30	3/16 × 1/24	1/4 × 1/30	1/4 × 1/24
6	44	42	40	37
8	38	36	34	31
10	34	32	30	26
12	31	30	28	24
14	38	27	26	21
16	28	26	25	20

Having measured the motor in its flat state and calculated the turns possible according to the table, the motor can then be skeined. This is a simple process and means that the number of strands is halved (e.g., for an eight-strand motor arrange in four strands at double length) and then while an assistant holds one end, the motor is wound in reverse to normal direction (anti-clockwise) for a nominal number of turns according to length. This will vary from 25 to 100 turns.

The assistant then holds the mid-point and the operator brings the two ends of the partly wound motor together. They are hooked on to the winder which is allowed to spin as the two halves entwine into a skein. Other methods entail winding up each half in turn, or taking one longer pair of strands and winding them to produce a tension, but the simplest method first described is most adequate.

The point of failure in a rubber motor is usually a few inches from one end. This is because the rubber has greatest strain imposed at about that point when fully wound *provided* that the ends of the motor are properly protected. Otherwise failure occurs far more easily at the extreme ends. Bobbins are sold to accommodate the various widths of rubber and will not only contain the motor ends in a convenient 'stack' but will also help to eliminate the rubber motor 'bunching' and so causing vibration. Their centre core is a minimum of $\frac{3}{16}$ in. thick so there is ample radius for the endloops to surround without a risk of overstretching the rubber at that point.

If a bobbin is not used, then the wire shaft must have a thick tubing sleeve over it (valve rubber, etc.) to avoid cutting. Some aeromodellers prefer to use an 'S' hook to prevent bunching, and this works very well indeed. Bunching of the knotted motor can ruin a flight and destroys much of the power available.

Lubricants

Similarly it is of considerable importance that the motor be properly lubricated. Several proprietary lubricants are on the model market, most of them good. They are based on soft soap and glycerine. Medicinal castor oil is another lubricant which does tend to 'disappear' and is certainly light for those motors which are to a restricted weight specification, as in the World Championship class where 40 gm. is the top limit for a *lubricated* motor. Modellers have preferences, and the keener types always wash out the motors if they are to be stored for a couple of weeks or more between outings. Rubber is inconsistent in quality. Some will withstand abuse. Another batch might lack power, and fail easily on less than full turns potential. In either case, extremes of temperature are harmful. Shield rubber motors from blazing sunlight, or freezing cold. If you have the time, let the rubber mature in store for as long as possible before use.

INTERNAL COMBUSTION

Whereas it used to be the case that a youngster or aeromodelling novice was 'weaned' to the hobby through the glider to the rubber-driven type, modern affluence is such that most are ready to leap into engine-powered flight straightaway. This is not such a bad policy provided the engine chosen is not difficult to operate. There are three forms of ignition in use for the miniature aero engine and they are all two strokes for the virtue of power to weight ratio (Fig. 8).

Spark ignition through a plug as used on all automobile engines, and employing a coil and condenser to build up the spark from dry battery electrical supply is a weighty business and by modern standards unnecessarily complicated. The system has inherent risks of malfunction at the three coil connections, two condenser connections or the insulated moving 'make and break' timing points which have to operate at up to 12,000 times per minute. There are certain places where the spark ignition engine has special attraction. It is controllable through the mechanical timing, over a wide speed range. The crisp exhaust note has an appeal to the modeller with an interest in engineering and electrics. The simple fuel formula of three parts petrol to one part heavy grade lubricating oil is easy and cheap to obtain . . . but if anything goes wrong, there are so many avenues to investigate! Unless one has a particular bent for this type of engine, and an understanding of the coil/condenser circuit, there is no reason to employ one. It was the introduction of the 'hot-wire' or **Glow Plug** for model engines in 1946 which completely eliminated the spark ignition system for all except the devotees. Hot wire was the very original form of internal combustion primer used by Orville and Wilbur Wright for their *Flyer* in 1903 when the first man-carrying powered flight was made at Kittyhawk.

It is simply a method by which a coil of wire remains incandescent within the cylinder head, and fuel mixture under compression explodes at reasonable timing when it comes into contact. The wire, which is platinum-coated in most cases to stand up to heat, is first heated by a short circuit. A 1·5 volt dry battery or 2 volt accumulator cell is connected across the plug terminals.

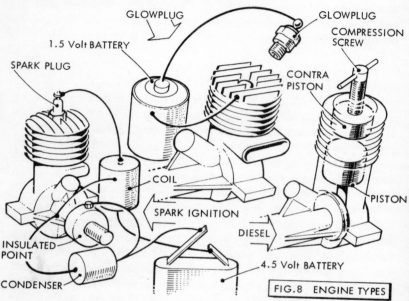

FIG.8   ENGINE TYPES

Special connectors are marketed for the various makes of plug, and once the engine starts, the battery should be disconnected to avoid overstressing the hot wire. One should also be careful not to apply the 2 volts of an accumulator cell to a plug designed for 1·5 volts—the plug will not last long under such circumstances. If one wishes to use the accumulator because of its good capacity then a simple dropping resistance is extra length in the connecting cable. 40 in. of flex is sufficient to drop the 2 volts to a safe output.

Glow plugs need a higher compression ratio (the ratio of swept to unswept volume in the cylinder) than for spark ignition although many such engines were easily converted to glow without any alteration other than change of plug. The ratio is in the order of 9 to 12:1 and the fuel is alcohol based. Methyl alcohol which is marketed as Methanol is the greater constituent, and simplest formula is 70 per cent Methanol, 30 per cent castor oil. This will produce average results, but for more flexible power range and to obtain peak power, additives such as nitro methane, nitro benzene and nitro propane are included as oxygen-bearing combustion aids.

Commercially-blended fuels are graded according to additive content, and in view of the fact that it is difficult to purchase small quantities of the chemicals most aeromodellers used the proprietary blends. Average cost of nitro methane, which is the best of the additives, is £1.50 per pint. Since up to 60 per cent is used in contest models for outright performance it will be understood that it is only the person who demands the utmost who will afford this cost of fuel for his hobby.

Starting the Engine

The procedure of starting a glow plug engine varies from type to type but in general, the tank should first be filled, and the level of the tank should be more or less equal to that of the needle valve on the engine. This valve is no more than a crude metering jet which controls admission of wet fuel to the engine.

The needle should be unscrewed to the position where it admits fuel by 'choking' (placing a finger over the carburettor intake and revolving propeller to draw fuel through the feed line by suction). Then 'prime' the engine by injecting a few drops of fuel into the exhaust port. Now flick the engine over several times in an anti-clockwise direction by pushing with the forefinger against a propeller blade. The engine is now thoroughly primed, and ready for ignition. Connect the plug. If a hissing sound is heard when the exhaust port is open, the engine is too wet *or* the battery is not delivering enough amperage. The plug should glow brightly and without sound after it has burned off fuel drops which may have become deposited in the prime.

After a few flicks, the engine *should* fire and continue to run according to the needle valve setting. If the valve is too far open (unscrewed) the engine will run slowly, erratically and emit exhaust smoke. If it is too lean (screwed in) then the engine will run only on the prime and then peter out. Needle valves are usually sufficiently flexible in control to give two or three turns complete tolerance. Remember NOT to run in an enclosed room, for carbon monoxide gas in the exhaust can be just as dangerous as with a large internal combustion engine.

If an engine appears to suffer from lack of compression, then a simple remedy to obtain easier starting is to inject a drop of ordinary thin machine oil in the exhaust port before priming with fuel. If a motor is persistently hard to start, look first for a loose or missing bolt in the crankcase. The two-stroke depends on crankcase seal in order to operate. If, for any reason, it is necessary to remove the plug for inspection, be careful to engage the threads properly when re-fitting as most heads are of light alloy and the steel plug can strip the threads if crossed.

Most commonplace form of model engine in Europe is the 'diesel' or **compression ignition** type (without a heat aid). This is a high (18 to 22:1) compression ratio unit which utilizes elements such as ether, paraffin and amyl nitrate or nitrate plus a lubricating oil in its fuel formula to give spontaneous combustion.

The compression ratio is variable by means of screwing down a contra-piston in the cylinder, or in remote cases by operating an eccentric shaft bearing. The engine is started on a high compression and when warm, and after the appropriate fuel mixture has been selected through the needle valve, the comp. ratio is finally adjusted. Though this sounds complicated, it has been proved many times that the novice accepts the 'diesel' far more readily than the glow plug engine in Europe. Certainly it runs with a dirtier exhaust (containing unburnt oil) and is prone to vibration; but the degree of control is better and the power for capacity (with notable exceptions) is better than for the glow plug engine.

Again, there are many proprietary fuels. A simple home-brew is to mix equal parts of ether, paraffin and castor oil. This works well up to about 8,000 revs. per minute then a misfire is likely as there is no smoothing agent. This is amyl nitrate or nitrite. Only a few drops per pint are needed (it costs about 30p per fluid oz.) and 3 per cent represents a saturation in even the most refined mixture for ultimate contest performance. As this is a heart stimulant, it is only available to responsible adults through a dispensing chemist.

STARTING TECHNIQUE

Starting a diesel is much the same as described for a glow plug engine except that one has to relax the compression screw (or tommy bar) in order to allow for the prime. The engine is easier to flick over smartly if the compression is so reduced and excess fuel is present. Then, when the engine fires and continues to run on the prime (which it will do for some time due to the inherent economic fuel consumption), the operator gradually increases the compression ratio to avoid misfire. The engine will soon warm up, and then the ratio is reduced again to the constant setting. Experience instructs the operator on the best balance of fuel needle valve control and comp. ratio adjustment.

Magnetos have been produced in miniature for model cars, and used most successfully for high-speed. Few aircraft models have used them, though the future of the speed type is very much controlled by means of ignition, and the development of the transistor may yet see transistor-amplified magneto-type ignition. It only needs an expert to get down to serious study of the technique.

There are features which are common to all the internal combustion engines, whatever their form of ignition. Firstly, they are either what is known as 'sideport' or 'rotary'. These terms apply to the induction timing of the carburettor and mean that in the first place the engine can be run in either direction, clockwise or anti-clockwise, and in the second case that the engine is timed for better efficiency and more power with the limitation that it will run in one direction only (unidirectional). Most engines are of the latter category and are timed to operate only in the anti-clockwise direction. Rubber-driven propellers are also arranged to run this way, the simple reason being that it is more natural to wind up the rubber motor in the opposite (clockwise) rotation for a right-handed person and also for the same person to flick a power propeller in the anti-clock direction.

POWER OFFSET

Because of this common factor with rubber-driven and power props, we are fortunate in having the same trimming characteristics in the model when flying. The rotating propeller generates a torque reaction which tends to pull the model to the left. As compensation for this, the engine, or noseblock in the case of rubber power, is offset to the right. This is call right-thrust. In addition, a small amount of downthrust is often employed to stop the power effect from throwing the nose up on a model that is otherwise aerodynamically trimmed for the slower, gliding flight after power has terminated.

It will be seen that with a unidirectional engine, a specially carved 'pusher' propeller is required. The requirement for offset still applies. On full size aircraft, torque is compensated by offsetting the fin rather than the power source, but the great difference is that the full-size machine does not have to return to earth without power or control, and fin offset on a model will result in a spin or at least, a spiral dive when power stops.

JETS

Most aeromodellers have ambitions for a scale model jet turbine but alas the scale effect, metallic needs and heat generated present serious limitations. A few examples have been made, only to burn out at the first run. What we can employ is the simple pulse jet. This is based upon the German V1 weapon power unit. It is little more than a shaped tube with valves at the front for ram air entry and a fuel supply. The unit is started by creating an explosion in the tube, and if fuel is being fed, the exodus of the first explosion out of the jet orifice will draw a second charge of mixture in from the front and so a second explosion takes place. The pulsing is constant, dependent on the design of the tube, and is generally faster on the smaller jets, slower on the larger. About eight different jets have been available, from Swiss, Japanese, German and U.S.A. sources. The noise of these units is so formidable that it creates a tremendous public resistance to operation within proximity of habitation, and the fire risks (the tube runs to near white-hot state) make the pulse jets prohibitive for free flight.

Thus it will be understood that the pulse jet is much in the minority. The record speeds of up to 190 m.p.h., and possibilities for actual scale models of real jet aircraft remain a great attraction for the aeromodeller who is prepared to abide by safety and noise abatement regulations. The facts are that one cannot have such enormous thrust of up to 8 lb. from a unit of only 15 oz. weight without an explosive system—and explosions are both noisy and fraught with hazard!

JETEX

The demand for jet simulation is considerable and after much research, the evolution of a dry fuel 'jet' which is in reality a rocket, came on the market under the name of *Jetex*. This is a small light alloy casing with special fittings and safety pressure valve to take pellets of I.C.I.-produced fuel. The fuel is solid and burns rapidly. The gas expansion from the burning fuel is directed through a small orifice and the thrust is greater than the weight of the unit by quite

1. Winner of the 1973 World Championships for free-flight power-driven models held at Wiener Neustadt, Austria was a local expert Vaclav Horcicka. His model had an Italian engine, turning over 22,000 r.p.m. during the 10-second power run which takes the model to over 600 ft

2a. (*left*) Joachim Löffler of East Germany became the World Champion for rubber-driven models in 1973—a performance he had achieved exactly ten years prior at the same Austrian site for this important biannual event. 2b. (*right*) Valery Ehktenov, the Russian model glider expert who won the World Championships in 1973. He achieved the best duration in final eliminating flights after a contest of very high standard. Thirty-three nations took part

3. Competition glider model to the Open class where no restrictions apply, taking advantage by use of large span and area to reduce wing loading. This one is known as 'Sunspot' and has many long flights to its credit

4. The sport power model is usually semi-scale in appearance, but has more generous wing dihedral for stability and an exposed engine for ease of operation. Known as 'Poppet', this one has a ·5 c.c. diesel engine and is very popular

a margin. Thus we can use Jetex for all forms of free flight since it is safe, almost noiseless and of adequate thrust. The limitation is that the duration of thrust is short, and this renders the unit unsuitable for control-line flight.

There is a variety of units, offering from ·4 oz. up to almost 6 oz. of thrust. Augmenter tubes can be added to increase efficiency, and by shaping the pellets at the risk of further shortening power duration, thrust is doubled in some cases (and *cases*, in some instances, melt with the extra heat!). Cost of operation is a nominal few pence per flight according to the size of unit.

Full instructions are given in the box, and additional tips which might be borne in mind are: Be certain that the unit is properly clipped in its mount in the same line of thrust as when last used (a deflection means a change of trim). Be careful to see that the orifice is maintained in a clean state. Replace the gauze filter frequently. Do not allow the pellets to get damp. Make sure that the igniter wick can easily be expelled from the jet. Cut the pellet surface like a 'hot-cross' bun to increase thrust if wanted; but be careful of overdoing this if the case is a standard aluminium unit and not the special heat-resistant type. Avoid personal contact with a unit directly after a flight—they get quite hot!

DUCTED FANS

Another form of model jet simulation employs the standard internal combustion engine, driving a small fan which is entirely enclosed within the fuselage. The thrust of the displaced air through the fuselage is not as great as that obtained from a normal propeller but not all that short. Models of same weight as would be for a given engine size for a conventionally-propelled type, can be flown but need to be smaller in size and to fly faster. All of which makes for greater realism and attractive performance.

Semi-scale jet models with ducted fans can even be radio-controlled now that fan design has almost approached the efficiency of the standard propeller.

The internal shape of the fuselage is as streamlined as possible to improve thrust, and the convergence of the tail cone, behind the fan, is to an area roughly 80 per cent that of the fan area. Small direction vanes are built into the rear cone to straighten the flow and to be adjustable for trimming the flight path for side, up, or downthrust action. Since the engine is enclosed, some form of starting has to be incorporated, usually in the form of a pulley to accept a cord which is wound round and pulled. Alternatively, a spring coil starter can be used.

The internal propulsion unit means that an undercarriage is not necessary for landing and propeller protection provided the under-belly is reasonably strong. In the same way there is no propeller to break on landing, and wings are arranged to detach on contact with any obstruction. So the ducted fan model is very much an approach toward the unbreakable. The drawback is that there is only one source of commercially-produced fans, and the experimenter must perforce make his own. Blades are from fibre, securely pinned within a fibre, light alloy or multi-ply core. They have to be carefully set at the same angle, and be of the same area to achieve a smooth vibra-tion-free balance. The pitch angle is a matter for experiment, 40deg. being the basic start.

Points which may not immediately be obvious are: The internal engine means internal deposit of unburned fuel, in consequence the rear fuselage weight steadily increases unless suitably protected and regularly cleaned. The engine access hatch should fit well, especially if it overlaps the area to the rear of the fan. The engine mount must be firm as there will be smallest possible clearance between fan tips and fuselage. The wings will have to be delta or swept shape in order to achieve proper balance without recourse to undesirable nose ballast. Ducted fan models always attract public interest, their realism and the 'mystery' of their propulsive system always draws a crowd. Since they also fly fast, one should be specially careful of accident risk.

We have only detailed the axial flow fan whereby air is taken in through the front of the fuselage and impelled straight through. There is also the centrifugal fan, mounted on its side which takes in air from the surface of the model and redirects it through 90 deg. or so to the rear fuselage. This is also very efficient and has advantages in small scale models but the torque reaction of the fan can produce unexpected results when the power stops. Flat spins are not unknown!

CATAPULTS

The simple yoke catapult can be employed in larger form for launching a solid wood glider but the initial thrust has to be damped.

MOTIVE POWER

We do this by having the elastic cord attached to a length of ordinary, non-stretching cord at each end. If, for example, we want to make a yoke-type catapult for a 24-in. span all-balsa glider, the elastic should be a 36-in. length of $\frac{1}{24}$ in. × $\frac{1}{4}$ in. flat strip with 18 in. of cord at each end, these ends tied to stakes in the ground.

Have the engagement hook at the nose of the model, hook on to the centre point of the elastic and pull back with the model as close to the ground and at slight angle of attack. On release, the lift of the wings will deflect the flight upwards, and the elastic will automatically disengage. Straight-line catapults are also usable but call for more elastic, say two strands, and the non-stretch cord.

Specially designed catapult-launched models have a device to stop them looping back on to the operator at high speed (Fig. 9). This is a

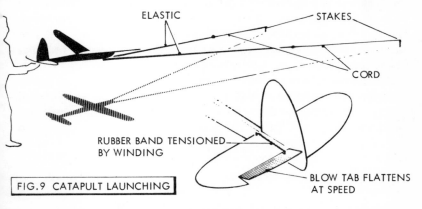

ELASTIC — STAKES

CORD

RUBBER BAND TENSIONED
BY WINDING

FIG.9 CATAPULT LAUNCHING

BLOW TAB FLATTENS
AT SPEED

tensioned elevator tab which is blown down by the high speed of the launch, then raises itself as speed falls off at the peak of the climb. 'Blow tabs' are very handy and enable very fast and thrilling flights with heavy models; but beware of accident risk. Speeds of over 100 m.p.h. have been recorded with catapult-propelled models.

ELECTRIC POWER

Until the advent of super-efficient electric motors in the late '50s, electric free-flight models were an impossibility. The problem is that of power to weight. Motors must be capable of working at fast speeds with good torque and at comparatively low drain. At the same time the electrical source from a battery or accumulator has to be light in weight. Lead acid cells suffice with a good motor in a light model but for larger models and better performance, nickel-cadmium cells, silver chloride water activated batteries and similar power sources are the rule.

The motor has to be a small one relative to the model in order to conserve weight. It *must* therefore be a very good unit, preferably with an integral gearbox if it is to drive the size of airscrew for best results. Only motor which meets this demanding specification at time of writing is the German Siemens which is selected for model work and marketed by Graupner as the 'Micromax'.

The author has been experimenting with this motor and many variations of special electric power design for over ten years, trying various power supply methods. Most exciting experience came with the use of a battery pack produced by the McMurdo Instrument Co. of Ashtead, Surrey. This was of the silver chloride type, where layers of metal are separated by lint and one injects plain water to activate. (McMurdo are renowned throughout the world for their batteries which are exclusively used for rescue purposes on life rafts, etc.). The 4·5V battery which weighs barely ¾ oz. gave enough power to zoom the model up at such a rate it rivalled a model with internal combustion engine, and flew for 6 min. on a motor run of only 20 sec. duration (Fig. 10). Other batteries which have given very good

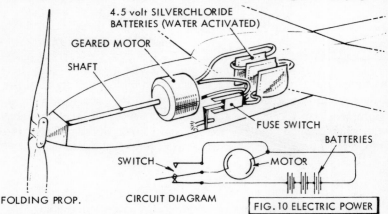

4.5 volt SILVERCHLORIDE BATTERIES (WATER ACTIVATED)

GEARED MOTOR

SHAFT

FUSE SWITCH

BATTERIES

SWITCH

MOTOR

FOLDING PROP.

CIRCUIT DIAGRAM

FIG. 10 ELECTRIC POWER

performance are the 'Magnalux' or 'Rulag' sealed lead-acid cells which are paired to give 4 volts, and the Japanese 'Yuasa' cells which are smaller and less powerful editions of the McMurdo type.

Some designs take advantage of the specially geared 15:1 electric motor by allowing the motor to run at its peak of electrical efficiency and thus taking the full power potential for the large propeller. This is almost half the wingspan (about 40 in.), so gaining a lot of valuable slipstream effect off the wings with extra lift. For the experimenter and the person who seeks the fascination of something 'different' the electric power model has particular charms.

The late Colonel H. J. Taplin made a radio-controlled electrically-powered model of over 7 ft. wingspan. This had a government surplus motor and a huge batch of Venner cells. Cost of the power supply was enormous, but the sense of achievement clearly outweighed the consideration of £30. All-up weight was 8 lb. In 1973 Peter Russell adapted a motor designed for model boats and flew electric-powered radio control at a very practical weight.

In Japan there has also been great commercial interest in electric power and several model kits have appeared. The Mabuchi motors are comparatively simple. They have to drive smaller props and are fitted with smaller airframes so in turn the performance is more of the amusement standard. Some kits are produced in expanded polystyrene and require only the assembly of the general components. Thus they serve as an ideal introduction to the hobby and with rapidly rechargeable Ni-cad batteries, the Japanese model designs will inspire deeper thought into the class of electric power as something for the future. The day will undoubtedly come when it will be both a competition class and a popular 'toy' product with clip-in rechargeable batteries for plastic moulded ready-to-fly designs.

Mattel, the huge toy corporation in the U.S.A., combined with Mabuchi of Japan to produce the electrically-powered 'Super Star' in 1972. The ready-to-fly model was so outstanding it made a nonsense of many other experiments, and from its pioneer effort the Mattel and Mabuchi 'Super Star' will generate more advanced designs for radio control.

CHAPTER 4

◎

Flying a Free-flight Model

◎

The major difference between a free-flying model aeroplane and its full-size counterpart is that the model is inherently stable and the real thing needs a pilot aboard to maintain stability. The model is 'trimmed' for all attitudes of flight from full power at launch to the gliding descent and the full-size is 'trimmed' by the pilot according to the power settings and required flight attitude.

If a model is out of trim, then naturally enough it will not fly satisfactorily and from the visible symptoms of instability one should be able to apply the corrections needed. There are elementary procedures. In a glider one can add ballast weight to the nose to avoid stalling, or alternatively, shift the wing back to obtain the same effect. Conversely, one can move the wing forward, or reduce nose ballast weight to prevent a dive.

LONGITUDINAL STABILITY

Choice of the airfoils for the wing and tail, and the exactness of their construction in the lifting surfaces, will offer a wide range of appropriate trim setting from model to model (Fig. 11). It is normal to have 'close' settings on a fast-climbing contest power duration model with the difference in angle of incidence between wing and tail only a degree or so. The model is then arranged to have a high wing position on a pylon and the centre of gravity is to the rear part of the wing, from 80 per cent aft. All of this is for the purpose of obtaining a fast rate of climb and to control excess power.

Conversely, the duration glider has a difference of up to 5 deg. angle of incidence between wing and tail, with low tail-wing area percentage (15–25 per cent) compared with the power model having 33–50

54

per cent tail area. The centre of gravity on the glider may be anywhere between 33 per cent to 60 per cent of the wing chord.

Much the same settings apply also to the rubber-driven model; but for a sport-flying power model, the centre of gravity is more likely to be between 25 per cent and 33 per cent of the wing chord measured back from the leading edge.

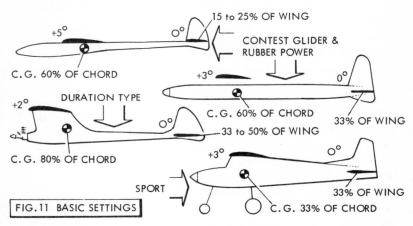

These are generalizations. Any well-produced commercial design either in kit form or sold as a plan will have the *designed* angles and centres of gravity (balance point) shown.

What happens as the model is being made, covered and doped determines whether or not the model will fly 'off the board'. An over-enthusiastic application of sandpaper on one leading edge will change the airfoil and lifting characteristics on one wing half. Slapdash sandpapering on spars and trailing edges can induce a warp. Equally, a curved building board will produce curved wings and twists. The accuracy of construction is important and unless the wings are true and warp free, or at worst, equally warped, one cannot hope for good flying.

Presuming that one has done one's best and the model is balanced where designed, it should glide to earth from a forward hand launch, without a stall or dive. The speed of the launch must be sufficient to obtain a normal flying speed for the model otherwise the symptom indicated may not be true.

If the model tends to soar up, then lose speed, and drop its nose in a dive, it has stalled. The difference in *effective* wing and tail angles of incidence is too great. First trim the tail surfaces. For a stall, one has to lift the tail leading edge to make the angle more positive. Trim with balsa packing $\frac{1}{32}$ in. thick and if this does not cure the stall, make the packing $\frac{1}{16}$ in., but beware that the angles of wing and tail do not become identical. An easy check is to use a piece of sheet balsa with a sighted straight edge. Place this under the wing surface and allow it to project back under the tail. One can then view the tail angle.

We *must* have the angular difference for longitudinal stability. If a model with its wing and tail each set at say, 3 deg. angle of incidence, is upset by a gust and sent into a dive, it will have little chance of recovery, as the tail will no longer have a suitable correcting force to act about the wing.

A model may appear not to want to fly. Each launch might result in a dive. This can be due to wing warp again, reducing the effective wing angle so that the tail is actually at a positive angle in relative attitude. The answer in such a case is to lift the wing leading edge. Tail trim will not be sufficiently drastic.

In the case of a model with a small tail, as for example of a scale model, the wing should be reduced in angle, rather than the tail increased should the model stall. Very often the scale type reveals a wing that is badly matched with a poor tail and the solution is to arrange a forward centre of gravity, as well as to reduce wing angle. This helps to eliminate the built-up stall which starts gently then gradually increases in violence until the model is virtually hanging on its propeller for one moment then vertically diving. An additional cure, should this symptom show up on powered flight only, is to apply 'downthrust' on the engine by packing washers under the holding bolts so that the engine is deflected down. Power is then utilized as a longitudinal stability factor.

A further aid is the pendulum-controlled elevator. This is a hinged elevator surface with connection to a pendulum weight near the centre of gravity. As the weight swings back and forward, so it affects the elevator through a small range of deflection. Thus if the model dives, the elevator is deflected up for recovery and vice versa. The danger is that without safe trim limits, such a system can lead to unfortunate build up of stalls through delayed recovery action. Answer is to conserve ambition and restrict the elevator movement to a few degrees for the first tests.

If a model persists in stalling, despite all the advised forms of correction, the final resort is to scrap the tail and build a bigger one, preferably having a cambered lifting airfoil. It is always essential that the tail shall remain effective after the wing has stalled and lost lift, otherwise it will not provide the means of longitudinal stability we require.

The subject is one that can be stretched to considerable technical lengths but fortunately the free-flying model is usually a most forgiving and tolerant device so that the basic information just given suffices for almost every case.

LATERAL STABILITY

Model aeroplanes are characterized by their large amounts of wing dihedral angle (upward and outward sweep of the wings). This 'vee' form is the first requisite of lateral stability. It provides a means of lift distribution so that should the model yaw (or be slewed in flight) or be deflected into a sideways bank, the unequal vertical presentation (viewed from above) of the effective wing area is sufficient to provide a correcting moment. So if a model has ample dihedral, it should enter a turn in a natural bank and if deflected, will right itself. This can be seen in a stall, if a model loses flying speed and drops one wing first, it may even roll on to its back. Dihedral throws it back on to an even keel as flying speed is regained.

Too much dihedral causes a model to oscillate or rock sideways, and this same symptom can be given by too small a vertical tail (fin and rudder). So if large dihedral angle is used it must be balanced by large fin areas.

A model may show a tendency to roll. This will be due to unequal angles on the wing through warps. At high speed, these angles will have more effective differences in *lift* and at low speeds, the *drag* effects will be noticeable. Thus a glider will turn one way when being towed up fast, then the other way on the glide which will be at a reduced speed. The warp affects lift at the higher speed and this is the principal cause of a model glider 'weaving' while on the tow-line.

Airspeed also determines the amount of fin area wanted and this is why the glider has smaller vertical tail surface area. A model which has insufficient fin area will enter spiral dives easily and will show obvious instability in direction. It may meander in either direction of turn and this is not desirable. The disposition of lateral area on a model has been the subject of much argument among experts. There is a 'centre of lateral area' theory which calls for a balanced side projection (including allowance for the dihedral on the wing panels) whereby if one were to make a card silhouette of the model, it should balance at a point in line with the centre of gravity and about 33 per cent back along the line between the C. of G. and the tailplane. This is a rule of thumb approach which produces good results but usually depends entirely on where the centre of gravity finally appears!

Too much dihedral angle creates a sideways rocking motion known as 'Dutch roll' and too little dihedral induces the spiral dive and slip. Since the lift of the wing will be affected by dihedral, we get the compromise of the glider with its large and long flat centre section to the wing with 'tip dihedral' and the 'polyhedral' of the fast climbing power model. Some modellers have even gone to the extreme on gliders and done without dihedral, using instead, deep tip fins to prevent loss of airflow at the tips and to compensate the side area.

Additionally, the expert modeller will deliberately warp his wings to achieve a certain trim (Fig. 12). The term 'washout' is not what

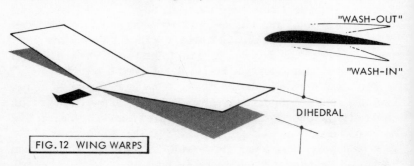

"WASH-OUT"

"WASH-IN"

DIHEDRAL

FIG. 12 WING WARPS

may initially be interpreted! It implies that the effective angle of incidence on the wing is *reduced* (trailing edge lifted) towards the tips. Conversely, the term 'washin' implies that the angle is increased. Power modellers employ washin on the starboard (right) side panel of their wings near the centre. This increase in angle creates extra lift during the fast climb, and compensates the inclination to roll, or even induces a roll opposite to the natural direction. Thus the model is aided in its climb. On the glide, this reverts to drag effect and controls the direction of turn (to the right). Washout at the tips is a stall delay device, for it is advantageous that any wing upset by gust or variation of airspeed, should have a wide speed range. Thus if a wing without the washout were to be stalled, the whole area loses lift violently. With washout, the tips remain effective and are corrective.

DIRECTIONAL STABILITY

All free-flight models are trimmed to fly in the most advantageous circling flight, usually to the right because thermal currents north of the Equator rotate in that direction (as does also your bathwater when running out of the plug hole). Some measure of directional stability derives from the features already mentioned for lateral stability, namely the dihedral and fin area.

For the power-driven model we have to offset the torque of the engine for powered flight, yet have a circling glide. Torque offset for the power-driven and rubber-driven model was detailed in Chapter 3; but the way in which the engine and fin or rudder settings are used together is a technique which deserves careful attention at this stage for so many novices go wrong here.

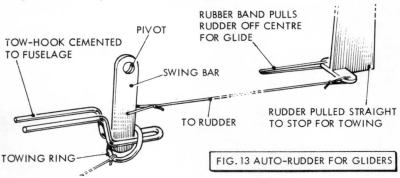

RUBBER BAND PULLS
RUDDER OFF CENTRE
FOR GLIDE

PIVOT

TOW-HOOK CEMENTED
TO FUSELAGE

SWING BAR

TO RUDDER

RUDDER PULLED STRAIGHT
TO STOP FOR TOWING

TOWING RING

FIG. 13 AUTO-RUDDER FOR GLIDERS

The rudder (it may be only a small trimming tab or the whole vertical fin) is the prime control for directional stability in the glider. It is gradually offset stage by stage until the desired circle is obtained. At the same time one can usually trim the tail into greater negative angle to keep the nose up in the turn and improve the rate of descent.

When the glider is launched on the towline, however, an offset rudder is a most dangerous beast. We have already discussed how the increase of speed in the towing creates quite a different warp effect in the lifting surfaces. Now, the rudder has greater effectiveness during the tow and the model will not achieve full height on the line. It veers off to one side, even to the stage of crashing. In consequence we employ the 'auto-rudder'. This is a very simple arrangement of pulling the flight rudder straight while the model is on the towline. A cord, connected to the rudder bar, is pulled forward by attachment of the tow ring. Thus the glider has two rudder settings, straight for the launch, turned for the glide (Fig. 13).

The sport power model is first hand-launched without the motor running and the rudder is set gradually as with a glider. When the desired glide turn and rate of descent are found, power flight with the motor set straight is checked. By fuel limitation or by using a commercial cut-off timing device, only a short power run of a few seconds is needed to indicate whether or not the rudder setting for glide is good enough for the climb. If it is not a fast model, little change should be necessary. Otherwise one must offset the engine in the direction shown essential. It may be that the glide rudder is too much for climb so the engine thrust has to be offset in the *opposite* turn direction to compensate the effect. With a powerful engine fitted with a large propeller, the torque will be strong and this may be adequate compensation (Fig. 14).

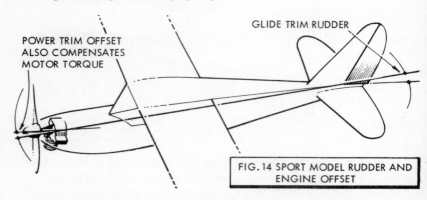

POWER TRIM OFFSET ALSO COMPENSATES MOTOR TORQUE

GLIDE TRIM RUDDER

FIG. 14 SPORT MODEL RUDDER AND ENGINE OFFSET

On contest-type power models, large rudder settings for glide are dangerous so an auto-rudder similar to that used for gliders is employed and is tripped about half a second before the timer cuts off the engine. The tail is also tilted so that its lift 'envelope' is inclined to one side (to the right) and this acts as a turn compensator in some cases or as a means of obtaining a left-hand climb turn in rare instances. The usual trim is for right climb and right glide circles.

The radio-controlled model is the only type which we really want

FLYING A FREE-FLIGHT MODEL

to have fly in a straight line when 'hands off'. For course flying in
contests, and for general local field flying, a straight direction model
is the ideal. This is most difficult to achieve. Long tail and nose
moments with large fin area are the first essentials but the engine
power remains a flexible factor which varies from flight to flight. One
can at least endeavour to obtain the straight settings by employing
motor offset and sticking to the same type of airscrew, fuel and engine settings on each occasion. Rudder offset on a radio-controlled
model is neither wanted nor necessary, for it will be the controlled
rudder movement which will give the operator what he is aiming for.

STOPPING THE MOTOR

Clockwork-driven timers, modified from camera timers used for
delayed action photography, are employed to stop model engines by
various means. Most common is the strangulation of the fuel supply.
The timer is placed between tank and engine and a flexible fuel feed
line is squashed when the timer has run its allotted setting of 10 sec.
or so. Another method is for the timer to trip a shut-off valve in the
fuel feed line.

The very powerful engines which run at high speed and may be
damaged by the 'leaning out' of the fuel supply or not stop quickly
enough, are flooded by another method. These engines use a pressurized fuel system. Air pressure from the engine crankcase is
directed into the tank. This more than compensates for the fuel
supply rate and so the fuel is fed by pressure. If this same pressure in
the tank is suddenly released by the timer, through a conduit to the
open carburettor, then the flooding effect will stop the engine
immediately.

There is also the application of releasing the seal on the crankcase
of the two-stroke engine. This does not work on all types of model
engine, and simply serves to reduce power without actually stopping
the type of engine which has a large crankcase capacity.

Many sport fliers use a glass eyedropper or similar tube to meter
their fuel supply. If the eyedropper is graduated, then static tests
will give an average rate of consumption and one can easily time the
duration of the power run by releasing the model when fuel gets
down to a certain level. A coil of the translucent neoprene fuel
tubing also serves this purpose and can be ideally marked at consumption rate per second after tests are made. Remember that a

61

FLYING A FREE-FLIGHT MODEL

change of propeller will mean alteration of the needle valve control, and also a change in fuel consumption rate.

UNDERCARRIAGES

A model does not have to take-off ground; but because it is a *model* aeroplane it is considered best form to fit an undercarriage for appearance' sake and also for preservation of the propeller. A rise off ground (R.O.G.) take-off is most satisfying. If one has the local facility, then R.O.G. flights become the rule and this is especially so with radio-controlled models.

The contest type does not have to R.O.G. his models, and so dispenses with the undercarriage altogether. He may employ a wire skid to take some of the landing loads during a dethermalized descent when the tail is released to cock up at a 45 deg. negative angle and the model comes down almost vertically like a parachute.

Short grass take-off with power models of about 3 ft. span or more calls for a two-wheel gear, having the wheel axis slightly forward of the wing. If smooth take-off area is obtainable then the wheels can be brought back to a position just enough ahead of the centre of gravity so as not to cause a tip over when the tail is released. A three-wheel undercarriage is ideal for smooth landings (not on grass) and here the main (rear) wheel axis should be aft of the centre of gravity.

The rubber-driven model starts off with a considerable burst of power as the propeller is released and this will 'jump' take-off the model in its own length. All one needs for field equipment is a length of linoleum to lay over the grass. Here, the propeller is more fragile if it is from carved balsa and not of the folding type, so an undercarriage is to be advised, and its position is ideally just behind the noseblock where it can best act as a protector.

Retractable undercarriages are still much of a novelty except in the waterplane and scale classes. The model which takes-off water has a large drag component in the shape of the floats. Clever modellers have arranged for the float to swing backwards and upwards so that it retracts against the fuselage and becomes streamlined as distinct from a detached mass. A fuse is placed between rubber bands that will hold the float down, and when the fuse is burned away it destroys the bands, and so permits the float to be pulled up.

FLYING A FREE-FLIGHT MODEL

GLIDERS

We have already discussed some aspects concerning the tow-launched glider but not the actual relationship of the balance point and the tow hook positions on the fuselage. This depends on the kind of airfoil and speed of flight but in general, the hook should be on a line from the centre of gravity projected at 45 degrees forward and down from the horizontal. This means that with the traditional shallow fuselage for higher performance gliders, the hook is not far forward of the C. of G. and for deep fuselages, the hook is fairly well forward. The skilled contestant has a towhook that is adjustable according to wind strength so that on calm days he tows from a point practically on the C. of G. position, and in strong wind he can shift the towhook forward an inch or more. The object is to tow the model kite fashion and to have the line near vertical for maximum height gain at the moment of releasing with a flick on the line.

Towline operation is quite a skill. Experts can run all over a field in search of thermal currents which will lift the glider up and stretch the line tight, then take the model off at a good rate of ascent. They can run upwind or crosswind but this activity demands an excellent physical condition and an intimate knowledge of the model characteristics.

KEEPING THE MODEL IN VIEW

When a thermal current takes a model to comparative high altitude, visibility is important. Bright colours are recommended, red being popular and 'Day-Glo' sections help enormously. The critical matter is that one must remember that in most winds, the model will drift in a direct line and if a dethermalizer happens to fail, or is not good enough, then a line of sight should be fixed with points on the horizon. Then concentrate on following the flight circles to see on which side of the sight line the model was last observed. It is a question of searching (after due permission to enter property has been obtained). One must concentrate on watching the vanishing speck if there is to be any chance of recovery. Once distracted, the modeller rarely regains the location of a very distant model. Flashes on silver paper fin reflectors have helped many a recovery. The paper from cigarette packets will adhere well with an impact cement and is very light in weight.

63

FLYING A FREE-FLIGHT MODEL

Most important is the name and address label. All models should have their owner's identification clearly marked in a prominent position, together with the offer of a reward to the finder. In comparison with the cost in time and cash for a replacement, a generous cash reward is not out of place for a prized model.

STRENGTH IN STRUCTURE

All the successful aeromodellers are those with a natural logic. They examine reasons why things happen and retain a commonsense attitude. One must always bear this in mind when a structural failure occurs. Weigh up the situation carefully. Look at the fault from different viewpoints. Was it bad construction or bad structure? Right material? Inferior flight trim? Answers to these pertinent questions will provide the clue to real success.

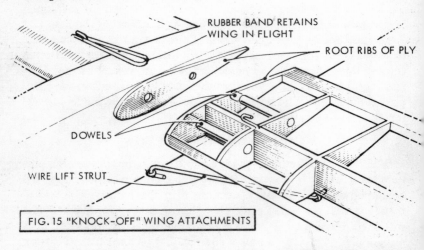

RUBBER BAND RETAINS WING IN FLIGHT

ROOT RIBS OF PLY

DOWELS

WIRE LIFT STRUT

FIG. 15 "KNOCK-OFF" WING ATTACHMENTS

Use hardwoods such as spruce for spars wherever possible. Sheet cover the leading edges of wings back to the mainspar on power models and gliders to get the correct airfoil section. Use sheet balsa fuselage construction as a labour saver and for durability in handling. Use sheet tail surfaces where a built-up structure is unnecessarily complicated. When a model crashes, recall the exact sequence of events in order to sort out the reason for the misbehaviour and apply the correction. If a particular component appears to be weak, don't waste time and effort in making it good in the same state as before,

5. Indoor model to international specification with a wing span of 90 cm., weighs little more than 1/20 of an ounce! Capable of making 35-minute flights in an airship hangar, it moves at less than walking pace and could be plucked from the air by its Finnish designer. Covering is microfilm

6. Ducted fan radio-control model with the engine hidden inside a hollow fuselage driving a fan impeller for 'jet' effect. Radio receiver is in the nose, batteries in cabin and rudder actuator above the tailpipe

7. Scale models of full-sized aircraft are a real challenge to ingenuity in design and construction. These demanding aspects are minimized in the kit model, one of which is this Robin
'Regent', made from a kit supplied by 'Practical Scale', a British manufacturer. The model is
radio-controlled.

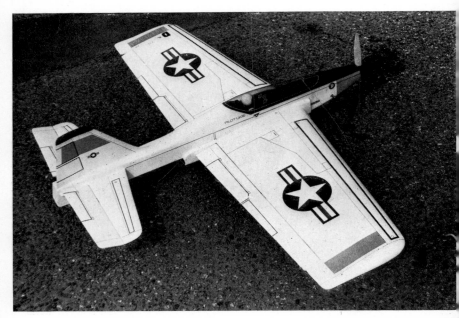

8. The control-line aerobatic model takes on a realistic appearance when panel and control
surface lines are marked, and international insignia applied. This design by German modeller
Claus Maikis is called 'Commodore' and is popular in Britain.

be prepared to make a new component of improved structure. It is often a wise notion to make parts 'knock-off' under crash impact. Wings can be located on short stubs of dowel and held in place with rubber bands. A wire 'lift' strut stops them folding up in the air, yet on landing, they will detach from the fuselage if any object catches a tip. Similarly a one-piece wing should have freedom to slide forwards or aft on a fuselage without damaging itself on the fuselage (Fig. 15). Rubber bands are, of course, the finest shock absorbers; but design logic is the basic essential for good model strength.

FAULT FINDING

The following gives a rough guide as to what might be wrong with a free-flight model.

Symptom	Correction
Repeated stalls with power	Add downthrust, reduce engine or rubber power.
Repeated stalls on glide	Move C. of G. forward, increase tail incidence.
Fast, flat flight, no climb	Remove downthrust or increase wing incidence.
Turn too tight	Use sidethrust, check wing warps.
Tendency to loop	Induce a turn with rudder tab, sidethrust or tilt tail to right (left tip up).
Stall when power stops	Check rubber motor for 'bunching'—reduce length of motor. Make glide follow same power pattern.
Dive on glide	Check rubber motor for 'bunching'—reduce length of motor. Shift C. of G. aft, lift tail trailing edge. Trim for glide then use upthrust.
Spiral dive on power	If turning right, use left turn. Cure with wing trim tabs, reduce rudder angle.
Spiral dive on glide	Check for offset drag effect (prop blade to one side only, etc.), check wing for warps.
Zooms when coming into wind on turns	Move C. of G. forward, increase tail area, lengthen effective nose movement.

65

CHAPTER 5

───────────── ◉ ─────────────

Control-line Flying

───────────── ◉ ─────────────

Flying a model on tethering wires, with the ends connected to a pilot's control handle and an elevating device in the model, is the most popular type of aeromodelling. This is because of the difficulty in obtaining space for free-flight models and the modern desire to have more direct control over the model. Chapter 1 gave us a breakdown of the various categories.

First and foremost, one must ignore the 'brick on a string' opinion which has often been expressed. The control-line model is, in its modern form, as dependent on its surface area lift and streamlining as any free-flight design. Admittedly one has little concern over lateral stability, but there is still a great call for careful arrangement of forces in order to obtain the balance and overall stability for the particular type of control-line design.

All have a common need for an offset centre of gravity. By this we mean that in plan view, the C. of G. should be to the outboard side of the fuselage centre line in order to balance the weight and drag of the lines. Additionally the large stunt model with up to 700 sq. in. of wing area, needs to have this area dispersed asymmetrically so that the inboard wing is larger and carries the weight of the lines with its extra lift.

Another common factor is that all have the pivot point of the controlling bellcrank in such a position that the C. of G. is forward of the pivot, often even forward of the front control-line, so as to maintain line tension.

Other stability aids are motor offset, fin offset, line sweepback and differential flap movement. All of these items are expressly intended to give good line tension under all conditions, for without a steady pull on the lines one does not have control (Fig. 16).

The degree of control varies according to the type. A fully stuntable model will have both the wing flaps and the elevators moving 45 deg. up and down. A speed model needs only 10 deg. up elevator and about 2 deg. down. A team racer has to have reasonable manœuvrability so 30 deg. up and down is common and this same range applies to the combat type.

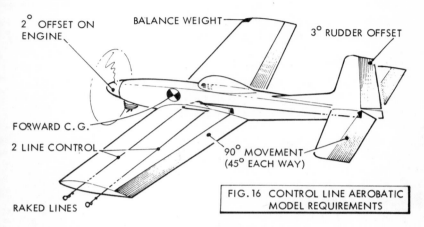

2° OFFSET ON ENGINE

BALANCE WEIGHT

3° RUDDER OFFSET

FORWARD C.G.

2 LINE CONTROL

90° MOVEMENT (45° EACH WAY)

RAKED LINES

FIG. 16 CONTROL LINE AEROBATIC MODEL REQUIREMENTS

Wing loadings vary from 8 oz. per sq. ft. on the aerobatic models to maximum allowable 32 oz. per sq. ft. on the International class speed entries. Airfoils are universally symmetrical and of low drag shape, and the fuel supply specially arranged to cope with the centrifugal force, often by using a pressurized tank. Taking the approach to modern control-lining in a practical series of stage by stage steps we should first start with the assumption of no previous experience.

First Flights

One should select a trainer with solid structure for the first attempt to 'pilot' a model. It could be a ready-made all-plastic model, or one of the specially marketed kit designs with solid balsa wings. Either type has forgiving characteristics and yet will teach the pilot many a lesson through mistake.

This is the only way to learn, for although direct instruction from an experienced control-line flyer is to be advised there is no substitute for the experience of an accident, and what can be better than an accident that can create no real damage?

Trainers have to be robust for this reason. The newcomer gets the impression that control-line flying is ridiculously easy, until he tries for himself and overcontrols badly! The first flight nearly always ends in a nosedive, but by five or six launches, the 'pilot' is really enjoying climbs and dives under complete control.

First make absolutely sure that the line connections are secure. Have the controls set up so that when the arm is outstretched and the wrist directed at the model, the elevator is at neutral position. Keep the wrist stiff in relation to the arm and lift the whole arm. The elevators will move up. Have the helper lift the model and one will observe that as the model comes up to the level of the pointing arm, so the elevators gradually adopt neutral position. This is the key to a successful first flight. Use rigid arm action, and point the whole arm exactly where the model is supposed to go (Fig. 17).

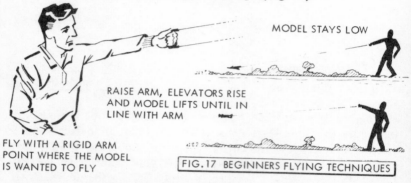

MODEL STAYS LOW

RAISE ARM, ELEVATORS RISE
AND MODEL LIFTS UNTIL IN
LINE WITH ARM

FLY WITH A RIGID ARM
POINT WHERE THE MODEL
IS WANTED TO FLY

FIG. 17 BEGINNERS FLYING TECHNIQUES

Check the engine, have it running slightly 'rich' then take up the handle the right way around so that 'up' is up, and *not* down! Then signal to the helper to release the model for take-off as the arm points at the model. When speed builds up, after about 20 ft. ground run, lift the whole arm and the model will follow. Don't panic and push the arm down again or you'll have a nosedive! Keep the arm pointing where the model needs to be (up in the air!) and the flight will have no more dangerous a manœuvre than a rather wavy level circuit.

Gradually feel the model control out as each flight encourages more confidence and in no time at all, climbs, dives, wingovers and loops are enjoyed. The dizzy reaction of the first flight is quite natural, and one soon gets used to the rotation within a few flights. The major danger is that of over-confidence. The motto of 'If in doubt, give "up",' has saved many a C.L. model from disaster.

CONTROL-LINE FLYING

The manœuvre which creates most havoc is inverted flight. Here one executes a half loop then by correction, holds the model level and upside down, with all control actions reversed as 'up' now becomes 'down' and vice versa. This is a test for will power. Some weaken and twist the wrist so that the handle is still acting in a natural up and down manner relative to the arm, and many flyers have the handle horizontal during all level flight so that there is but little difference in reaction either way up.

LEARNING TO STUNT

The fully aerobatic model is as different to the trainer as is the full-size fighter and the *ab initio* trainer. Livelier controls, with quicker reaction, faster flight and greater power reserve all add up to a jump in technique that calls for caution on the first flight with a new model.

First of the stunts to learn is the wingover. This calls for a bisection of the circuit with level half lap. The model is obliged to turn sharply into a vertical climb from low level, is flown up and over the top, then vertically down to a sharp pull out in low level flight. This is progressively attempted from shallow climb through steeper angle climbs to the ultimate. It calls for good co-ordination, ability to control when sight of the horizon is lost, and the pull-out demands confidence. Later, one can attempt an inverted pull-out for the *reverse* wingover where a half lap of inverted flight divides two wingovers.

Next, the loop. This calls for height judgment and sensitivity of control. One has to swing the whole arm around following the loop so that it becomes one smooth, round loop and not a lemon! Over controlling causes a 'mush' on the pull-out, even a stall. Variation in control action gives a jerky flight pattern and wrist action rarely gets the desired effect. Consecutive loops can be attempted after one has confidence that the first loop is completed without loss of speed or height, then the outside loop should be considered.

This is started either from level inverted flight or from the top, down. Either way, the model seems to be heading for destruction as the nose tucks under, and first attempts nearly always end up in a wild tug at down elevator for an over controlled pull-out. Once started, the outside loop presents no greater difficulty than the normal inside loop, and after the initial reaction to having the fin point-

69

ing to earth, the pilot soon becomes acquainted with the manœuvre to the extent of really enjoying it.

Inside and outside loops made side by side, above one another, overhead and 'four square' make up the rest of the aerobatic schedule except for 'square' shaped manœuvres with horizontal and vertical sides joined by corners of smallest radius. Once one has mastered the loop, then all other aerobatics become a case of developing the techniques.

In order to achieve finesse in the smoothness of control and accuracy of positioning, the model design becomes subject to various novelties, all of which have become fashionable though not necessarily advantageous in all cases. The inboard wing panel is always larger in order to compensate for line drag and weight. The flap on the inboard panel can be made to swing through a wider arc relative to the outboard and this differential maintains line tension. The flaps *and* elevators each move at the *same* ratio (maximum of 45 deg. up and down) to get the 'square' manœuvres. Rudder area is large, nose moment fairly great and tail moment short. Above all, the very important fuel tank is large enough for a 6-min. duration and well placed and designed for a constant supply.

The tank is usually fitted with a baffle to remove the ill effects of surge, and the ventilating pipes are so arranged to have a forced air feed.

In the author's view, apart from radio-controlling a model with the full range of control surfaces, the aerobatic control-line type offers a greater satisfaction than any other model aeroplane. One has a special satisfaction in being able to execute aerobatics at very low altitude, and the direct pilot-to-model control through the wires is as near as one can get to full-size flying without actually sitting in a cockpit.

FLYING IN WIND

There remains one important distinction between control-line flying and free flight which is often overlooked and as a result, creates many a disappointing crash. This is the effect of wind. A free-flight model will drift *with* the wind, and travels downwind at a ground-speed relative to windspeed. Once launched, even in strong wind, the free-flight type will perform in much the same manner whether the wind is 5 or 28 m.p.h. (Fig. 18).

CONTROL-LINE FLYING

The pilot of the control-line model, at the centre point of the circling flight path, is fairly stationary. Thus the control-line model has to pass upwind, downwind and crosswind on each circuit. It speeds up and is slowed down by the amount of windspeed, and will have to have corrective control applied as it circuits. Otherwise it

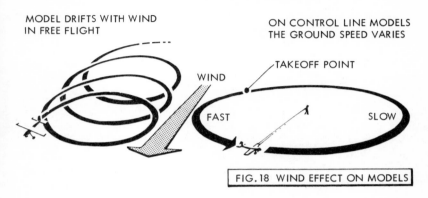

MODEL DRIFTS WITH WIND
IN FREE FLIGHT

ON CONTROL LINE MODELS
THE GROUND SPEED VARIES

TAKEOFF POINT

WIND

FAST

SLOW

FIG. 18 WIND EFFECT ON MODELS

will climb into wind and dive downwind. Take-off should always be on the crosswind leg so that the model is accelerating to full centrifugal force as it flies downwind. The lines will remain tight in these circumstances but if the model is permitted to take-off into wind, it will balloon up at too early a stage and without control due to slackness in the control lines.

This applies to *all* classes of control-line model but is more critical with the comparatively lightly loaded aerobatic designs.

Speed Models

It is now possible for speed models to exceed 200 miles per hour in record attempts! This is strictly for the specialist who will spend all his time in tuning the engine or pulse jet and obtaining special fuels. Speeds of 160 m.p.h. upwards are commonplace at National Championships with the 5 and 10 c.c. engine capacity categories.

The International class has removed much of the advantage which certain nations have in the availability of fuel constituents such as tetranitromethane which is a highly toxic oxygen-bearing chemical guaranteed to improve any glow plug engine performance. Instead, the International class requires use of one of two fuel mixtures.

CONTROL-LINE FLYING

Either 80 per cent methyl alcohol and 20 per cent castor oil or a 75 per cent, 25 per cent mixture of the same two basic contents. Additives are outlawed, though the diesel engine is free to have what it can best use. Structurally it is at a disadvantage and has top revolutions per minute (r.p.m.) limitations, so even the most refined diesel fuel formula is usually inferior to standard fuel in a *racing* glow plug engine.

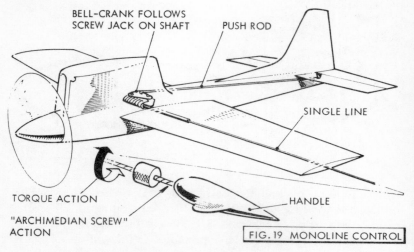

BELL-CRANK FOLLOWS
SCREW JACK ON SHAFT   PUSH ROD

SINGLE LINE

TORQUE ACTION   HANDLE

"ARCHIMEDIAN SCREW"
ACTION

FIG. 19 MONOLINE CONTROL

Since the object is to obtain fastest recorded speed over a kilometre course (over a certain number of laps at set radius) then streamlining is of utmost importance. The engine is totally enclosed in a cowling, normally rather like a helmet surround to the cylinder. Wing and tail junctions with the fuselage are most carefully faired in, and the areas kept down to the minimum allowable. For the International class this is about 80 sq. in. of total lifting area for the 2·5 c.c. engine. Similar size wings and tails are used for engines of four times this capacity but not always efficiently. The model still has to fly properly in order to be fast, and many speed enthusiasts make the grave mistake of thinking that a saving in wing area means reduction of drag. Often there is actually an *increase* of induced drag due to clumsy area reduction!

By far the greatest source of drag is the control line(s). They can absorb as much as 56 per cent of available horsepower according to a laboratory report. In consequence, line diameters are reduced to minimum allowable and 'Monoline', which is an American patented system of control with one line only, has such advantage that it has been used for practically every record flight (Fig. 19).

Unlike the standard bellcrank control, where push-pull action on the two control lines actuates a rod to the elevator via a bellcrank, the Monoline method uses torsion applied to the line which is twisted by a kind of Archimedean screw at the pilot handle. Torsional losses over the length of the thin line are such that many times the number of twist are applied by the pilot: but this in turn is to advantage as it offers an automatic gearing of control. In the model, a special 'Speed-master' unit converts the line torsion to push-pull action on the elevator rod, with mechanical self-centring through spring loading.

Monoline demands a different technique and even the most skilled two-line experts are obliged to return to training when they adopt this drag-reducing system.

Beside the racing engine, the streamlining of the model and the reduction of line drag, speed models also depend largely upon the fuel feed from the tank and the propeller. It is in these two items that we find 'fashions' from year to year.

Modern speed designs in Great Britain use a flexible tank made from a pen bladder. Fuel is pumped into the bladder, which then has the benefit of surface pressure to maintain supply of fuel and eliminates the need for airventing the 'tank'. Sometimes the pen bladder will have a balloon fixed around it, with a small degree of inflation so that the air pressure on the outside of the bladder also helps.

Elsewhere, the sealed pressure tank is used. This is filled, then sealed. A tube to a timed tapping on the engine crankcase takes air under pressure from the engine. This applies pressure on the fuel surface and replaces lost fuel with air in the tank.

A third system is the 'Chicken-hopper' tank. This has two cells, and just as with the battery-fed chicken water supply, the second (smaller) cell is filled only when and as consumption takes place. Balance of air in a ventilating pipe controls the flow from the main cell to the smaller compartment and the reason for the system is that by having a small cell, the fuel being used from that cell will not show variation in centrifugal force effect or gravity effect during the entire engine run.

As for propellers, these are really the make or break features of speed design for it is no use whatsoever attempting to obtain high

73

speeds without some refinement of the standard commercial propeller. Blades should be of true airfoil section, sharp at the leading edge, very smooth on the surface and flexible. This last value is a key to success for it allows a blade to take on greater effective pitch angle as the model flies. Whether the blades should be thin or not depends on the width. Remember that they are airfoils and must have some thickness in order to act as a lifting section for forward thrust.

The flying of a speed model is not normally difficult. Provided the C. of G. is ahead of the pivot point on the control system and the model is given the opportunity to take-off under control, it will give the pilot little trouble for centrifugal force is in itself a great stabilizing factor. However, in order to place all competitors on the same fair basis, a 'pylon' is used to locate the centre of the circle in relation to the control handle and to ensure that the operator does not apply any manual assistance to the speed of flight by 'whipping'.

The pylon is of special design, and for International contests, there are two designs, one for each of the control methods. Flying 'in' the the pylon is a very different matter to normal control, and *must* be practised before reaching the stage of entering an event. No longer does one have complete freedom of arm action, and the return to that arch-enemy of beginner tactics, *wrist action* has to be used in the pylon.

The speed model is small but involved. It is aeromodelling's closest approach to model engineering and as such it attracts a particularly 'mechanically-bent' section of those following the hobby.

TEAM RACING

Inspired by the closed circuit races held at Cleveland in America, model team racing is the use of three or four models to particular specification, flying simultaneously in the same circuit over a set distance. They race against one another, and fuel tank capacity is so limited as to demand a number of pit stops where refuelling and re-starting is conducted by the mechanic. Regulations vary in countries; but the general theme is for a Pilot/Mechanic pair to match their tactics of speed or range against the opposition. There is a very keen following, and despite the semi-scale appearance and need for an undercarriage, many team racers are fast enough to win speed model contests; 115 m.p.h. is not uncommon! It is in this class that British engines excel. They are universally employed in every nation where aeromodelling is practised as the best power units for team racing.

In Great Britain there are three classes. Smallest is Class ½A, where the wing area is 90 sq. in. for an engine size of 1·5 c.c. and 6 c.c. fuel tank. Next is Class A which is to the International Specification of 186 sq. in. total lifting surface, 2·5 c.c. engine and 7 c.c. fuel tank, and largest is Class B for 5 c.c. engines having a 30 c.c. fuel tank and minimum of 125 sq. in. of wing. Classes ½A and B are flown over 5 miles in the heats and 10 miles in the finals, while the International Class is run over kilometre distances of 5 kilometres for heats and the final at Championships, but with a 10 kilometre final at the British Nationals meeting.

Hare and tortoise tactics are common. Some models can almost cover the heat distance without a single pit stop but at slow speed. The gain is considerable but the possibility of having a mechanical failure through overheating or a poor engine setting at the start is too great a risk. Fastest models usually win. A pit stop can be completed in scant seconds, and times of under 6 min. for 10 miles and 4½ min. for 5 kilometres indicate the efficiency of pilot/mechanic teams.

It is the challenge of teamwork that has made team racing so popular. Keenness finds just rewards and it is one of the few types of competition where almost all of the entries remain on site to see the eventual winners.

As with the speed model, streamlining, tank design and the propeller are most important keys to success. What has been said for speed applies equally well to the team racer with the additional proviso that the engine has to re-start promptly in pit stops. The modern racer employs a single or 'Mono' wheel undercarriage as a drag reduction. This brings with it a need for clever pilot action in take-off and landing, especially at grass tracks. The retractable undercarriage is the ideal, and several experiments have been made in this direction. A gain of up to 10 m.p.h. could be expected from a streamlined retraction, but the gear has to come down again for the several landings, and that means a payload of one operating servo, batteries, etc. Electrical current can be passed along insulated control lines at some voltage loss, or extra lines used (though the drag would probably cancel any advantage in speed) but the ideal is to have a radio-controlled undercarriage, signalled as wanted by the mechanic. Significantly, this would only be possible with expensive superhet receivers, all crystal controlled in the allowed waveband, in order to give all teams the opportunity of having simultaneously retracting undercarriages. If the standard super-regen receiver were to be used, any pirate operator could signal an opponent's gear up or down at most embarrassing moments.

Team racing is a most involved subject and the specially interested reader is advised to obtain details of latest regulations from the S.M.A.E. offices. He should also study the section on team racing in *Control Line Manual* by the author, published by Model and Allied Publications Ltd., where performance tables are quoted to indicate the many avenues of tactical approach.

COMBAT

As the title implies, combat aeromodelling is the use of two or more models in the same circuit, all using same length lines (50 ft.) and towing streamers which are attacked and 'clipped' by the propellers. This exciting opportunity to allow one's feelings the full scope of aggressiveness at little personal risk, has attracted more aeromodellers than the other classes in recent years.

The modern combat design is a fast, flying wing, of robust structure, easy to make and very manœuvrable (Fig. 20). British rules

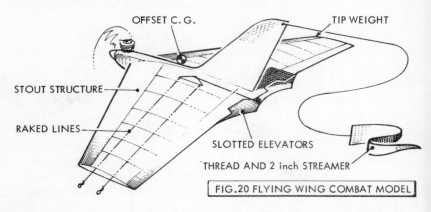

OFFSET C.G.

TIP WEIGHT

STOUT STRUCTURE

RAKED LINES

SLOTTED ELEVATORS

THREAD AND 2 inch STREAMER

FIG. 20 FLYING WING COMBAT MODEL

have a limit of 3·5 c.c. but in the U.S.A. and elsewhere the limit is ·40 cu. in. or about 7 c.c. Destruction is often absolute. Wins are frequently disputed. Points lost for time on the ground are usually the deciding factor in a heat. Reserve models are brought into the fray at a moment's notice. These are the pointers of combat, and they all add up to a lot of fun, especially for the man who feels he is not

CONTROL-LINE FLYING

efficient enough at team racing, speed or aerobatics but is quite capable of chasing an opponent's trailing crêpe paper streamer!

Hints for success are to use nylon covering of heaviest grade, very hard leading edges, to fly fast as possible even at the sacrifice of manœuvrability and to have a model that will fly 'eyes-off' when you are watching what the other man intends to do. For local field flying and club events, combat flying has a special attraction and is always a crowd pleaser at the fêtes and carnivals where clubs are asked to demonstrate.

RAT RACING

Despite its name, which has been adopted from the original American description, rat racing is not a form of matching rodents along a track for the benefit of bookmakers, it is a simplified form of team racing which accepts all comers. Stunt models, trainers, sportster types and special designs race against one another but have to land at least once each 70 laps. Only restrictions apply to engine capacity. No special airframe is required. Thus the class has appeal for clubs as an amusing event to add to the year's programme and the modern rat racer is not far removed from a team racer with exposed engine, crossed with a crude trainer. It might well be the kind of control-line model once used for running-in engines, a sort of 'easiest way out'. Nevertheless, despite lack of elegance, the rat racer returns great amusement for little effort.

FAULT FINDING

The following gives a rough guide as to what might be wrong with a control-line model.

Symptom	Correction
Engine stops after take-off	Carb. setting too 'lean' or tank not giving proper fuel flow under centrifugal force effect.
Model 'light' on lines, not responsive	Heavy lines, insufficient rudder offset, C. of G. too far aft. Alter these and add offset to engine plus outer tip weight.
Model over-sensitive, will not fly straight and level	Move C. of G. forward by adding nose ballast, reduce control sensitivity by lengthening elevator control horn.
Tendency to climb	One line is shorter than other, adjust lines.

77

CONTROL-LINE FLYING

Symptom	*Correction*
Model flies in state of yaw	Reduce engine and rudder offsets.
Slow reaction to controls	Bring C. of G. back, add tail ballast. Check control hinges for freedom of action.
Model flies 'banked'	Wing warps should be removed or inset ailerons fitted to compensate. Check elevators for equal angles if separated. Also flaps.
Refusal to take-off	Pick the control handle up the correct way!
Handle angle alters for 'neutral' during flight	Check bellcrank for wear or line ends for tightening and so reducing effective length.
Model soars into wind, dives downwind, getting progressively worse	Flying with too much 'up' elevator on an underpowered model. Try to fly with arm pointing at model for true neutral elevator at level flight stage.
Engine 'leans' out when model flies inverted	Tank position too high in fuselage, drop it relative to carburettor. Vice versa for a 'rich' engine symptom.
Lines stick together and jam	Line not properly unwound from reel. Replace lines completely, unreeling in-line with reel and not at 90 degrees to it.
Lines show engine vibration	Replace rigid piano wire lead-outs in wing with multi-strand cable (cycle 3-speed cable).

CHAPTER 6

---◎---

Radio-Controlled Model Aeroplanes

---◎---

It is the aim of practically every modern aeromodeller to have a radio-controlled model in his collection. Modern electronic design has produced a state of reliability in transmitter and receiver circuits so that anything which is to go wrong in a model nowadays is usually at the fault of the operator and is either electrical or aerodynamic.

Two wavebands are permitted by the British G.P.O. who issue licences of 5-year period for a fee of £1. The 26·96 Mc/s to 27·28 Mc/s band covers 99 per cent of the activities, and the higher frequency 468 Mc/s band (from January 1963) is limited in application due to the directional control and higher weight of receiver. There is, as yet, no Government requirement for crystal control of the transmitter as in the U.S.A.; but in any case all the reliable circuits incorporate a crystal for spot frequency.

One can break the radio equipment down into various classifications. First, the simplest is a **Carrier Wave** transmitter operating a **Super-regenerative** receiver. These are sold in made-up and kit form and are cheapest on basic cost. Depending on the degree of use of transistors, the weight and bulk of the gear in the model will vary from 5 to 11 oz. For reliability, a two-valve receiver with *current rise* of 4 milliamps or more, and actuators for motor and rudder control can be contained with 11 oz. of payload, and any airframe of 40 in. span upwards ought to absorb this.

The simple Carrier Wave set is subject to sensitivity control, due to high and low tension battery fluctuation. It is virtually obsolete in spite of its cheapness. The current rise of 4 milliamps is good at close range but reduces at a distance and may be marginal for some relay settings. With a **Tone Modulated** transmitter and **Audio Tone** receiver, the carrier wave is superimposed by a tone note and this

amplified tone note causes a change in receiver current to operate the
relay, the current change being considerable. Thus the Tone outfit
has greater reliability through being able to do without the sensitivity
control and having greater flexibility.

Furthermore, by adopting an all-transistor circuit, it is possible to
have a 3 volt tone receiver weighing only ½ oz., giving a total equipment weight in the model of about 3 oz. For this, one must of course
pay a price and the lightweight tone set with transistors eliminating a
relay costs about three times the amount a kit carrier wave set totals.

The next stage is the 3 volt **Super-heterodyne** receiver which is
virtually a miniature version of the domestic type set, with many
stages of amplification, lined up and preset so that the receiver is
virtually always on tune and rarely needs attention. In addition, the
Superhets are crystal controlled at spot frequencies of up to six in
the authorized band so that as many as six models can be flown together without fear of interaction and interference. This again, costs
more and is certainly beyond the scope of the amateur home constructor who seeks a kit for his radio outfit. But one must emphasize
that in terms of ultimate value in lower operating costs, greater
reliability, etc., it pays to invest in the best!

Thus we can see that there are three basic types of receiver. In
addition we have **single channel**, operating just one relay and a single
control as with *all* carrier wave sets and **multi-channel** for as many as
twenty controls. The latter is an extreme since twelve channels are
as many as a model currently can employ usefully.

All multi-channel sets have to be tone-modulated as the distinction
between channels is by means of the tone note. Sets have a low note
of about 300 cycles per second, and the bands are separated by 30 to
60 cycles up the scale. When heard over a monitor with loudspeaker,
the notes sound exactly like the musical note scale of *doh, ray, me,
fah, so, lah*, etc., and in the receiver there is either a **reed bank** or
special **potcore filters** to accept each signal. The reeds are like those
in a mouth organ and vibrate only when the particular note is re-
ceived. Where it is desirable to have simultaneous control action, two
modulators are fitted to the transmitter so that two reeds can actuate
at once.

Reeds, relays and filters all acts as switches to operate the electrical
circuit of an **actuator** or **servo**. If transistors are employed to replace
the mechanical relay, there is considerable saving in weight and
reliability.

RADIO-CONTROLLED MODEL AEROPLANES

An actuator is a device which will drive a control surface by means of a trip which 'comes-in' when a solenoid is activated. They were for a long time rubber driven for model aeroplane purposes, before the motorized actuator, which is more powerful (for boat rudders) became foolproof. The variety of commercial actuators offers one the choice of single acting left-neutral-right-neutral, or left and right selective with a single neutral, or full 'compounded' with additional controls added and wiper contacts to bring in secondary actuators for motor or elevator control.

The novice is advised to start with an actuator that simply gives right and left rudder alternately with self-neutralizing action between. Later he can readily graduate to the selective 'Compound' actuator which has the very great advantage of giving right and left rudder as selected—plus motor control if arranged. This demands a deal of care in signalling, not likely to be helped in the very first flight stages of the excited novice, hence the recommendation to stay simple (Fig. 21).

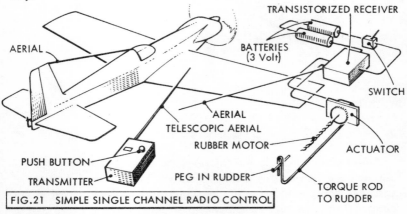

FIG.21   SIMPLE SINGLE CHANNEL RADIO CONTROL

The old-fashioned rubber motor gives an adequate number of commands per flight, and is surprisingly fast in action. In fact the 'compound' actuators have to be slowed down by incorporated ratchet to accept the signal distinctions. Fast control action is essential. A touch of rudder on a model will start a circle, and in 180 deg. of the turn, most models have their noses down for a spiral dive. To be able to correct quickly is most necessary.

The motor-driven actuator can be used on gliders or power-driven models. The supply market is shrinking, however, and almost all equipment sold now is for the selective servo system, known as 'multi'.

For multi-channel, motor-driven servos have been specially developed, many of them with internal transistor amplifiers to eliminate mechanical relays, etc., and costing about £10 each. These servos operate in either direction, and are linked to two channels each so that one servo will give left and right rudder according to which way the signal lever is pushed. Twelve channels would require six such servos on rudder, ailerons, elevator, motor control, elevator trim angle and either flaps or retractable undercarriage.

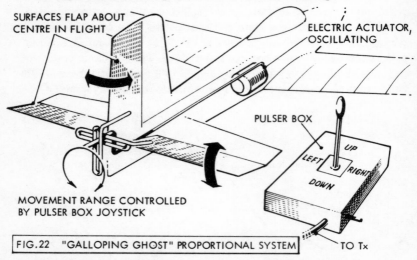

SURFACES FLAP ABOUT CENTRE IN FLIGHT

ELECTRIC ACTUATOR, OSCILLATING

PULSER BOX

UP

LEFT

RIGHT

DOWN

MOVEMENT RANGE CONTROLLED BY PULSER BOX JOYSTICK

FIG.22 "GALLOPING GHOST" PROPORTIONAL SYSTEM

TO Tx

Additionally there is an **Intermediate** class where two control surfaces are operated by a single channel. This can be by means of cascaded compound actuators working rudder, elevator and motor control through a telegraphed system of signals from a 'beep' box, or by the **'Simpl Simul'** system. The former utilizes a wiper contact in the control box to emit signals in set sequence. For example, in order to get down elevator by 'beep' box, one sends a *dot-dot-dot-hold signal*, which is very hard to execute accurately by thumb but easier by mechanical box. The latter 'Simpl Simul' system originated in the U.S.A. and is strictly single channel with a *proportional* servo which follows a joystick action at the transmitter. Since the rudder and elevator are interconnected on the same rotary shaft, each is obliged to flap about a centre point. According to the rate of pulse emitted (from 2 to 24 cycles per second) and the ratio of 'mark-space', so one gets proportional rudder and elevator (Fig. 22). When transmission fails or is switched off, the surfaces go to extreme limits with the most hair raising manœuvres as a result. However, the degree of control is remarkable and well worth considering. Commercial sets were marketed with limited success. Because the surface flapping does sometimes cause a light 'gallop' in the fuselage flight path, this system is generally known as **'Galloping Ghost'** in Britain.

Proportional control from a joystick is, of course, the absolute ultimate in most people's eyes, and the Digital system with proportional feed-back servos is established as the 'ideal' though expensive answer. Pulse rates are high so that the surfaces do not actually flap and any particular position of surface control can be held. The technique is superior to the manual pulsing one is obliged to do with a standard multi-channel set, but demands very careful technique. Control movements on a fast model have to be slight indeed for even quite vicious action! These systems range from one to six function units and form the greater part of present R/C equipment sales at model shops.

Those are the control systems. Their application is largely a matter of what purpose the model is made for, and whether or not the modeller is contest minded.

THE MODEL

For local field flying, one does not need the course 'flying' strategy demanded in contests. The model can be a conversion of a sport type, a scale model or an unorthodox type. It is usually required only to give fun to the operator and to return to his feet (or nearby) under full control. Low passes on slowed motor, with a blip of power for yet another circuit before landing are a joy to experience. The model will only be flown on suitable days and does not therefore have to be an all-weather design capable of forging its way through a near hurricane.

Similarly, it can get by with rudimentary control as distinct from the hairline control demanded in contests.

For these purposes one need only study the model for the following. Strength, easy of repair, accessibility of interior. The strength is called for because the engine will be running for longer periods than in a normal free-flight power model and vibration plus fuel soakage takes its toll. Ease of repair is required because the temptation of

RADIO-CONTROLLED MODEL AEROPLANES

radio control is to fly in small areas where hazards frequently get in the way; and accessibility is self explanatory. The same goes for single channel, multi or intermediate.

About 5 sq. in. of rudder, moving up to 5 degrees either side of neutral and motor offset to maintain nearly straight flight with neutral rudder are the basic general rules which apply to all sport models with radio control.

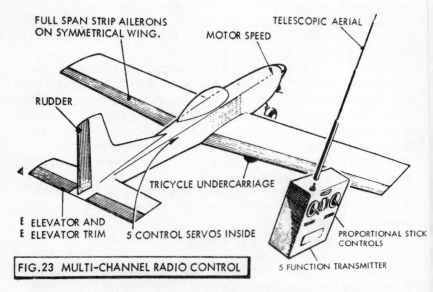

FULL SPAN STRIP AILERONS ON SYMMETRICAL WING.

TELESCOPIC AERIAL

MOTOR SPEED

RUDDER

TRICYCLE UNDERCARRIAGE

E ELEVATOR AND
E ELEVATOR TRIM

5 CONTROL SERVOS INSIDE

PROPORTIONAL STICK CONTROLS

FIG. 23 MULTI-CHANNEL RADIO CONTROL

5 FUNCTION TRANSMITTER

The contest model is a different type altogether. It has to be specially designed for the purpose. Light weight is important, constant speed through manœuvres and ability to execute left and right, inside or outside turns and loops of equal size and shape is critically important for each contest is for flight over a prescribed pattern and the winner is chosen by his excellence of control over the pattern.

Thus for single control (rudder with engine speed allowed) the technique is for a long-nosed model, able to penetrate wind and hold straight course, fitted with a powerful engine and *three*-speed control. Fast is used for take-off and to gain height between manœuvres. Medium is for the manœuvres and slow for the prescribed landing. The rudder is large and quick in action. It is forward balanced (with a rearward hinge line) so that it 'snatches', and a tricycle undercarriage gives a bounce-free landing.

RADIO-CONTROLLED MODEL AEROPLANES

For multi-channel, thick wings to obtain constant speed, full span ailerons, long tail moments for smoothness of loops and turns, short noses for manœuvrability and very accurate trim positions of the elevator for upright and inverted flight plus spins are all essentials. The multi-channel model is not flown by occasional selection of a corrective signal, it is flown *all* the time by a rapid series of manual pulses on the levers, so that surfaces just move a fraction at a time and repeated blips of signal on any particular surface control hold it away from neutral for a turn. Full signal is used for loops and spins only (Fig. 23).

INSTALLATION

The most obvious but so often disregarded aspect of radio control is that of proper and efficient installation of the equipment. Even when the gear is laid out neatly, a modeller will overlook elementary precautions and may have his receiver aerial alongside a wire rod, or several wire to wire joints free to rattle and cause interference. Logic is the keynote. Think matters out most carefully and never presume, *always* check everything twice over. Lash wires in place with thread so they cannot break soldered joints. Make sure that engine vibration does not affect the receiver by mounting it in foam rubber or Hairlok. Have servos and actuators fairly rigid so that constant neutral positions prevail and above all, plan the wiring harness so that there is not a rat's nest of wire in the fuselage and that all components can be de-plugged, removed and tested independently. Heaviest parts (batteries) go to the front, with the receiver so fitted that the radio frequency tuning is accessible without having to unpack the gear for a precautionary field check.

Remember that the radio-control system consists of YOU, the operator, a switch or lever, a transmitter and aerial, a receiver with batteries, another switch, relays, reeds or filters, servos or actuator, more batteries, linkage to the control(s) and the surface itself. That's a lot of system, and it allows plenty of scope for something to go wrong. All too often the radio is blamed when it may be engine vibration that is at fault, or any link in the system between YOU and the surface. Happily, most who take up radio control are inclined toward the mechanical and electrical knowledge which gives an advantage.

RADIO-CONTROLLED MODEL AEROPLANES

COST OF OPERATION

As to the cost, a simple 'single channel' set made from a kit, plus model with engine will cost about £25 minimum. A Tone Modulated outfit from a kit will be £5 more at least and if supplied ready-made, will cost £35 minimum for model and gear. A multi-channel model will cost at least £110 to put into the air. Some are worth four times that! The point is that the radio gear is usually tough enough to survive the model and can be used over a long period. Cost of operation is such that the multi-channel model costs less in battery expenditure than a carrier wave single channel type due to later developments. Fuel costs are heaviest, a multi-channel model using up to 10 oz. of fuel per flight, costing about 25p per flight at lowest rates.

To some these figures may appear exorbitant for a hobby. The rewards are nevertheless proportionate to the investment, and first sight of a multi-channel model flying through the 15-min. flight pattern at a competition will not fail to impress the most hardened critic.

SLOPE SOARING

Flights of 10 hrs. or more are possibilities with the radio-controlled slope soaring-model. This depends upon the standing wave of rising air in front of a prominent hill. The glider is hand-launched from

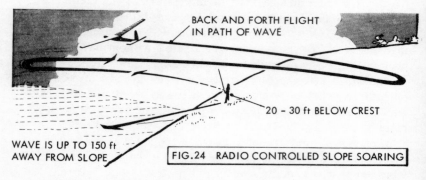

BACK AND FORTH FLIGHT IN PATH OF WAVE

20 – 30 ft BELOW CREST

WAVE IS UP TO 150 ft AWAY FROM SLOPE

FIG.24   RADIO CONTROLLED SLOPE SOARING

just below the hilltop, it glides out away from the hill, soars and is caught by the wave and held there, passing to right and left with nose into wind, under radio control (Fig. 24). This is a fascinating and little-appreciated aspect of the hobby. Contests are run so that each

86

entrant has a 5-min. period starting from release of the model. Points are debited according to the number of seconds above or below 5 min. to the time of landing. When it is realized that zero scores (i.e. no loss of points) have been returned over an average of three flights it will be seen that radio-controlled slope soaring has a great attraction—and it by no means approaches the costs of operation detailed for power models in the previous paragraph!

CHAPTER 7

———————————◎———————————

Scale Models

———————————◎———————————

The true scale replica of a full-size aeroplane has a very special attraction and when one realizes that the scale model can nowadays be flown in any of the modern aeromodelling categories of free flight, control line or radio control, it is not surprising that it is a popular branch of the hobby.

Many kits are sold for scale subjects and a vast plans range is marketed. These models are proved types, with small detail modifications to take care of the auto-stability we need. Tails are sometimes enlarged a small percentage and airfoils always have to be altered to better lifting types, or symmetrical for control-line aerobatics.

Free-lance designs, created from manufacturer's general arrangement drawings, are a fine challenge to the aeromodeller. One can start with a glider such as the wartime troop carrier Waco Hadrian, or more refined sailplane, the Olympia, and then on to the light planes such as the Auster series, the Pipers and Cessnas.

For rubber drive, longer-nosed machines such as the Pilatus Porter with turbojet Astazou engine are perfect and novelties like the twin boom Lockheed Lightning give an opportunity for the modeller to get out of the conventional rut.

Jetex power simulates the jet. The Sabre, Hunter, Attacker, Phantom or Lightning (English Electric this time) are all perfect for mounting a Jetex unit internally or in a belly trough.

Ducted fans give the opportunity for greater realism with larger jets, but the choice is usually limited to those with fuselage intakes in the nose and circular section fuselage.

The subjects are innumerable. They can be historic (Lindbergh's 'Spirit of St. Louis'), spectacular (Richthofen's Fokker triplane), or staid and stable (faithful Tiger Moth). Whatever the choice of subject, some consideration has to be made as to its suitability for a particular application.

If it is to be a power-driven free-flight model (perhaps with radio control) then the tail area should be at least 18 per cent of the wing area for a monoplane or 12 per cent for a biplane, and should be made of lifting section if less than 20 per cent in either case. If the nose is short, select a heavy engine to get useful balance without having to resort to wasteful ballast. Check the size of the engine cowl. Will your engine fit inside? Is the cowling a radial type with large frontal area to create drag? Is the dihedral angle on the wings adequate for lateral stability?

These questions are the basic considerations. One must also view the subject from a practical modelling aspect. Is it possible to reproduce the shape of the fuselage as on the full-size machine? Would the structure be adequate for rough handling and landing? Vulnerability can be compensated by use of 'Knock-off' components, and since the scale type will only be flown as a sport model in conditions of the operator's choice, it will quite naturally enjoy a fatherly attention.

DESIGN CONSIDERATIONS

Having chosen the subject for a particular form of power, the first and most important design consideration is to determine the weight permissible, and this in turn defines the size of the model.

A *glider* should be loaded at about 5 oz. per sq. ft. of wing area. This means that if we choose a Hadrian as suggested earlier, and the span wanted is about 48 in., the wing area will call for a total flying weight of about 11 oz. and this will give a most reasonable gliding angle.

A *Jetex* model will be limited in weight according to its power unit. The 35 size should be in a 1½ oz. model, the 50 in 2 oz., the 100 unit in a 4-oz. design, the Jetmaster (or Payloader) takes 5 oz. easily and the 350 unit 7 oz., while all of them should have a wing loading of about 6 oz. per sq. ft. of wing area.

Same wing loading of 6 oz./sq. ft. applies to the *rubber-driven* model, so here it is really a case of choosing how large one wishes to make the model, then working out the weight permissible from the area.

The *control-line* model is more flexible in weight consideration. The wing loading can be between 10 and 16 oz. per sq. ft. according to whether the type is supposed to be aerobatic or not. Lightest load-

ing is for the aerobatic stunter. There should also be a power loading
to ensure that the model will be reasonably powered and this is given
a top limit of 8 oz. per c.c. of engine capacity. So, for example, if the
engine is 5 c.c., then we are allowed up to 40 oz. of model weight.
Taking this maximum weight and dividing it by the load factor we
get a permitted 360 sq. in. wing area. Now one has to decide on the
nearest convenient scale which arrives at about 360 sq. in. wing, and
it will be somewhere near to ⅛ scale for an 'average' fighter type.

Free flight should have a power loading of about 20 oz. per c.c. of
engine capacity as a maximum and a loading according to the real
aeroplane character ranging between 6 and 16 oz. per sq. foot of wing.
Taking the example of a 1 c.c. engine in a Cessna 150 light plane, we
have a ceiling weight limit of 20 oz. If we set 8 oz. per sq. ft. as a
target for a reasonably slow and stable model, then we need a 360
sq. in. wing. As with our control-line example, this means about ⅛ in.
or 1½ in. representing each foot scale model.

The *ducted fan* model has to fly fast for efficiency. It has a higher
loading on the wing, and a lower power loading for thrust. 10 oz.
per c.c. is a top power loading limit and 12 oz. per sq. ft. an average
wing load.

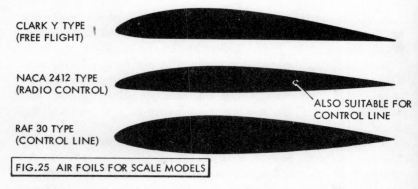

CLARK Y TYPE
(FREE FLIGHT)

NACA 2412 TYPE
(RADIO CONTROL)

ALSO SUITABLE FOR
CONTROL LINE

RAF 30 TYPE
(CONTROL LINE)

FIG.25 AIR FOILS FOR SCALE MODELS

Then one must view the shape of the aeroplane, having determined
the size and weight for available power, from the aerodynamic set-up.
The wing will invariably need alteration of airfoil. For free flight and
radio control, the flat-based Clark Y airfoil is a favourite. For control
line, the near symmetrical NACA 2412 or completely symmetrical
RAF 30 and for fast-flying models, a choice of any of these airfoils
thinned to about 60 per cent of normal (Fig. 25).

SCALE MODELS

Wings for free flight and radio control are set at about 3 deg. positive angle of incidence, and the engine must be offset with right thrust for most high wing models. Downthrust is applied to stop the high wing type 'ballooning' when turning into wind and tending to stall, while upthrust is sometimes needed for the low wing aeroplanes.

The tail should be set neutral to the fuselage datum line, giving an angular difference between wing and tail of about 3 deg. for free flight. In control line, no such angular difference (longitudinal dihedral) is wanted, all surfaces are parallel to the fuselage datum and the thrustline.

PLAN ENLARGEMENT

For the home designer, the most difficult part of scale modelling is usually the enlargement of the plan from a small three-view. This can be tackled in many different ways.

Easiest (and most expensive) is to have the plan photographically enlarged by the *Photostat* process. This is used by industry for drawing enlargement and is developed to a very accurate stage. However, it does not maintain a constant line thickness and naturally all the original lines are thickened by the degree of enlargement.

It is far more satisfying for the astute modeller to produce a fine line pencil drawing of what he wants, and tackled carefully, such draughtsmanship can be as pleasant a recreation as the actual making of the model. The point is not to treat the work as a task but more as a means to obtaining the best standard for one's final product.

There are at least seven quite different ways by which an enlarged drawing can be produced. Simplest and most attractive is by means of the *Pantograph*, a method which is generally well known but which calls for a degree of unappreciated skill. It is a simple lattice work that connects a pointer and a pencil in a ratio of motion. One end of the linkage is firmly pinned to the board, and the pointer moved about to follow the contours of the small drawing. In so doing, the pencil, which is at the end of the linkage, moves through a proportionately enlarged range and traces the same outlines only larger. All mistakes and inaccuracies are similarly enlarged. If the Pantograph is accidentally shifted, it must be re-located accurately. This last word is the keynote to successful Pantograph work.

Proportional dividers are the next most attractive instrument and in fact they are the best to select. All measurements are proportionately

91

enlarged according to the ratio of their setting on the dividers, and by dealing in dimensions, there is less likelihood of error. Curves have to be plotted in stages and outlines sketched in but in general the proportional dividers are ideal for modellers. Being precision instruments, they cost from £3 50 upwards. Limits are that one should not enlarge with the 'scissors' set for more than a 5:1 ratio in one stage. Otherwise the extreme scissors angle of the instrument will not allow an accurate enlargement.

Of course, one can manage with a pair of *Compasses* by simply spacing off each dimension so many times, but this too creates an enlargement of any error. Or, one can set to with paper and tables to *mathematically enlarge* by calculation.

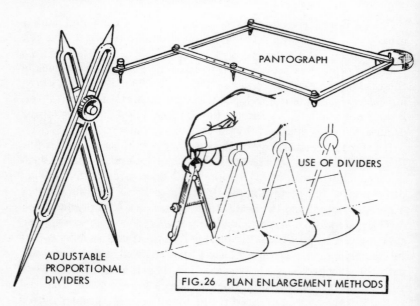

FIG.26   PLAN ENLARGEMENT METHODS

Another alternative is to obtain a set of *Scale rules* which are cheap and card printed for about five different scales per set.

In practice, the application of proportional dividers, multiplied measurement by calculation and French curves for outlines, offers the best solution (Fig. 26).

The most important aspect is to make absolutely sure that the small-scale plan is correct in the first place!

SCALE MODELS

STRUCTURAL DESIGN

The flying scale model differs only from the conventional flying model in that it has to retain the appearance of the full-size and also be practical. This means that the thin wings of an early biplane call for use of hardwood spars and ply parts or that a fuselage which was fabric covered over stringers must have similar model structure. Weight grows rapidly as such detail is reproduced. One has to apply logic and strike an average somewhere between what is desirable and what is practical.

Small dimension stringers do not offer a lot of strength so for this construction a basic box fuselage is usually made with the formers and stringers superimposed. Metal covered 'stressed-skin' wings and fuselages have curvatures on the full size that can only be reproduced in scale with sheet balsa planking. This is done in strips, each tapered and bevelled to match its neighbour then the protrusions sanded off to a smooth exterior. It sounds difficult but is not, the art being to use soft balsa and squeeze it into the gaps. A covering and a filler will give all the desired appearance of the real thing.

Arrange for 'knock-off' wings with clip fittings to retain them while in flight, but be sure that the wing angle is firmly set before each launch!

PENDULUMS

Lack of dihedral, or smallness of the tail area is the penalty which most scale subjects have to overcome. Cheating the difficulty by altering scale appearance will often spoil an otherwise perfect replica. In order to obtain the flight stability needed for free flying, the pendulum-controlled tail surface was applied to scale models (Fig. 27).

The elevator can be connected directly by pushrod to a suspended pendulum weight near the centre of gravity. As the weight is disposed, so it will move the elevator up or down. In a dive, the weight swings forwards, and the pushrod pulls 'up' elevator. Range of motion should be small.

The rudder is affected by sideways motion of the pendulum, and is similarly actuated by a pushrod. Danger is that excess rudder correction can sometimes create a spiral dive. Two or three degrees of motion is sufficient to correct.

93

Ailerons can also be pendulum operated and all three control surfaces actually interconnected. By this stage, however, radio control

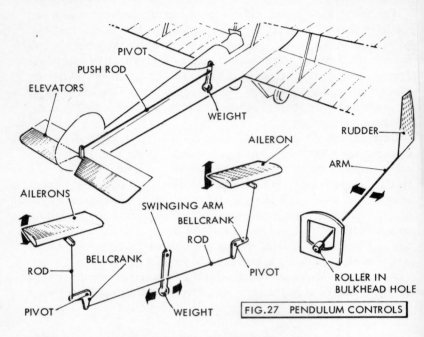

FIG.27   PENDULUM CONTROLS

steps into the picture with far more satisfying and less risky results.
When a subject needs so much mechanism to obtain a reasonable
stability, it is hardly likely to last for long!

CONTROL-LINE POSSIBILITIES

Without need for any stability considerations other than in a horizontal plane, the control-line model offers exciting possibilities in
scale. Retractable undercarriages, bomb dropping, lighting, engine
speed control, landing flaps and lights are but few of the many
operations one can have through extra lines or by using the existing
control lines to pass electric current to the model.

One can race replicas of actual full-size racers in team race style.
Or conduct aerial battles with small-scale World War II fighters.
Subjects which could never be considered for free flight are within
the scope of control line. Wing loading allowance shoots up, and the

greatest need in stressing is to ensure that the wings will take the
landing shocks. Wingtips have been known to drop suddenly when
a model has hit the ground!

Colouring always adds a lot of weight and it is in this field that the
control-line type shows special advantage. The cockpit can be fully
'equipped' and metal cowlings actually made in metal as distinct
from weight-saving paints. Dummy radial engines, using the actual
model engine cylinder to represent one 'pot', always add to appearance; and use of control-line cable with model ship fitting turn-
buckles to represent scale rigging on a biplane is weight that can well
be afforded.

Dummy pilots in the cockpit, with clothing applicable to the type
and authentic colouring and marking round off a well-prepared
scale model.

One does not have to be an expert. It is sufficient to have enthusiasm and the asset of patience to make a good scale replica.
When reasonably experienced in model making and conversant with
control of a conventional model, it is most certainly possible to
reproduce famous aircraft like the Battle of Britain Spitfire II or
Messerschmitt Me 109 for proportional radio control and to have
them flying in mock air battle together through use of the fixed
frequency receiver. In fact it was this very suggestion in the first
edition of this book which inspired the film technicians to use radio
controlled models for dogfight and crash scenes in the film 'Battle
of Britain'.

CHAPTER 8

───────── ◎ ─────────

Unorthodox Models

───────── ◎ ─────────

We have become so accustomed to the aeroplane with wing(s) set about one-quarter way back along a fuselage and horizontal and vertical tail surfaces that virtually every other form of flying machine is classified as 'unorthodox' (Fig. 28 indicates a variety of subjects).

Even the transposition of wings and tail in the *Canard*, or tail-first machine is considered unorthodox although in fact it is as stable a system as one could want and has been in existence since the first ever man-carrying flight by the Wright Brothers 'Flyer' in 1903. The Canard is fascinating and will become more familiar when transonic airliners appear in this form. The nose-plane becomes the trimming surface, though elevators are incorporated in the mainplane trailing edge, and it is normal to have a pusher engine. Only in centre of gravity location is the Canard at great variance with convention. Balance point should be *between* the nose and mainplanes somewhere within the range of midway to the actual mainplane leading edge according to the purpose of the model. Free flight calls for an aft position near the wing, control line needs a forward balance, up to mid point.

Machines which flap their wings in an effort to emulate the birds are called *Ornithopters*. They can be powered by rubber motor or internal combustion engine, and have a mechanism which transmits power to the wing roots so that the panels oscillate in unison. Since there is an optimum rate of 'flap' which is still a rather slow beat of about 60 to 100 per minute, it is difficult to regulate the miniature engine-powered ornithopter with a satisfactory gearing, for normal useful revolutions per minute of these engines are about 8 to 14,000. In consequence there have been very few successful powered ornithopters. Those which set up records in Germany during 1938,

96

9. Aim of many modellers is to produce a radio-controlled scale type such as this Hawker Hurricane which has rudder, elevator, aileron and motor control. It is extraordinarily realistic in the air and has Battle of Britain Eagle Squadron markings. It is capable of executing most known manœuvres

10. The Rogallo flexible wing which is after the fashion of a kite set at 15 deg. angle above the fuselage, can be a most exciting model project. This particular one has made many flights to over 500 ft. and is fascinating to watch in the air

11. Unorthodox control-line aerobatic model is a canard, or tail-first type, with the engine arranged as a pusher at the rear. Controls in this case come between wing and noseplane which carries the elevator. In addition there are flaps on the wing

12. Unusual type is the tailless model as displayed by this British contingent flying at a Dutch international contest. Wing sweep and change of angle at the tip provide inherent stability

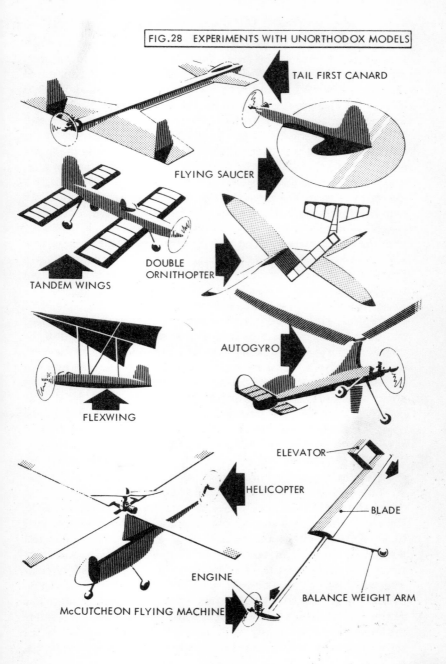

FIG. 28 EXPERIMENTS WITH UNORTHODOX MODELS

TAIL FIRST CANARD

FLYING SAUCER

TANDEM WINGS

DOUBLE ORNITHOPTER

AUTOGYRO

FLEXWING

HELICOPTER

ELEVATOR

BLADE

ENGINE

McCUTCHEON FLYING MACHINE

BALANCE WEIGHT ARM

with flights of 10 miles, were really gliders with an engine driving a small flapping vane at the nose. The configuration would not pass modern specifications. Indeed, later thought which has been inspired more by the butterfly than the bird, is sufficiently advanced for us to discard the German experiments, for the biplane type of ornithopter has had surprising results. Instead of just two wings, each raised and lowered simultaneously, we can have a double pair each side of the fuselage, acting in converging manner and thus improving the thrust effect considerably. One major disadvantage of a single pair of flapping wings is that thrust is intermittent, and height gain usually a matter of chance. The butterfly type offers a genuine rate of climb with continual thrust. Light weight is essential, and the actual wing panels are flexible so that they can deflect up and down in sympathy with the spar movement. The leading edge is usually the main spar and the shape of the tissue panel such that when deflected, it will form the most useful curvature for lift and thrust. It is inevitable that the final appearance is bird or butterfly-like.

One can add extra wings to a monoplane, making it a triplane or *quadruplane*. Though less efficient due to interference between wings, and because the area of each wing should be about one-third of the area normally given to a monoplane with same size tail and fuselage, the 'Quad' gives a very good account of itself as a sportster and will surprise many a fellow modeller. Each wing should be spaced at about two-thirds chord apart and staggered by one-third chord. This means that the distance from bottom of lower wing to top of the upper wing will be equal to two wing chords at least and the trailing edge of the upper wing will be over the leading edge of the lower wing. The balance point should be arranged, using the mid position between centre wings as a normal mean chord. Solid sheet balsa wings are quite acceptable for such a 'Quad' of up to 35 in. wingspan.

The all-wood model is, of course, an easy approach to experiment. It removes the time-consuming covering stages and at the expense of some efficiency, allows the germ of an idea to be realized and test flown very quickly. In this way, an elementary *Flying Saucer* or circular winged craft can be made in an hour or so. The circular wing is little more than a derivation of the delta, and the airfoil should be accordingly similar with generous reflex at the trailing edge. The section is formed by a centre fuselage across the 'Saucer', this holding the curves which are easily made across the spanwise grain of the sheet balsa wing. As the circle will have to be made up of butt-joined

98

sheets of wood to obtain the diameter, it is possible to add shape-forming ribs at the same time and so do without a centre fuselage. Treated as a delta or tail-less model, the flying saucer should balance between 30 and 50 per cent of the wing root chord from the leading edge, according to the purpose of the model. Free flight has the aft C. of G., and control line needs a forward balance.

Many configurations are possible with the simple all-sheet balsa 'chuck' glider. The *Tandem wing* machine where the fuselage is rather short and wings are disposed at extremities though of almost equal size, is a fascinating experiment in stability. This type of model will be very difficult to stall. It accepts a good range of balance positions, and given reasonable dihedral angle, will fly on a rock steady path. Its main disadvantage is this 'solid' stability which reduces its ability to quickly recover from any upset. Should the model enter a dive, it will take longer than a normal wing and tail model to recover, and may even continue on its flight path in a dive. A Tandem wing has no practical advantage over other shapes, although it has been exploited in France as a means of obtaining a low wing load and high lift for flying on low power. Classic example is the '*Flying Flea*' configuration where the two wings almost overlapped. Control was on the angle of incidence on the upper and forward mainplane, a system that was not blessed with the natural reactions of elevator and rudder control and which became the downfall of the full-size 'flea' in Great Britain. As a model subject, the flea arrangement is satisfactory for slow speed flight in calm air, using rubber drive. Washout of the wing angles toward the tips and generous dihedral is advised.

FLEX WINGS

We can really extend the experimental shapes of model wings in all directions. There is only one limit to observe, and that is a correct balance of the lift, drag, thrust and gravitational forces. Once this relationship was established in the U.S.A. by the N.A.S.A. scientist Francis M. Rogallo for a type of flying kite which he called the '*Parawing*', then all sorts of flexible aircraft wings began to appear. The N.A.S.A. issued three informative technical documents on the subject of the flexible wing patented by Mr. Rogallo and these provided inspiration for others. In Europe, Dornier were first but others followed. In the U.S.A., the Ryan Company made the first man-carrying '*Flex wing*' with an engine and propeller, then came home experiments with towed gliders and kit sets.

Critical factors are roughly that the angle of leading edge sweep should be 50 deg., the balance should be 40 per cent of the root chord which can also be the same length as a leading edge, and the angle of incidence should be about 15 deg. relative to the thrustline. The fuselage should be about one-quarter wing root chord from the mid point of the chord, suspended below, and bracing must be applied to keep the wing square to the fuselage in the head on view. As for 'ballooning' effect, this is easily obtained in the following manner.

Non-porous material such as a Polythene (as sold coloured green for sunshading glasshouses, etc.) should be cut to a square, the sides of which are equal to the required leading edge span. Use aluminium tube for the two leading edges and root chord, and lay the root tube across the square from one corner. As this will be equal in length to one side, it will fall short of the diagonal distance across the square. Trim the Polythene sheet so that the extremities of the leading edges (at corners) and the root tube are joined in straight lines. Now we have to make a bracket to fix the three tubes together at the common corner, and bring the angle of sweep in to 50 deg. from the 45 deg. of the square. Attach the Polythene securely by wrapping and welding with a soldering iron (use a heat insulator to avoid direct contact) or use an adhesive such as 'Pac'. By reducing the sweep 5 deg. each side of centre we have an automatic 'ballooning effect' on the wing panels. A lateral brace across the tubes can hold the sweep angle. Such a flex wing is remarkably tough and is fascinating to see fly as a glider or power model. When it lands and forward motion stops, the wings collapse and can be folded if the lateral brace is made to unhitch.

It is this configuration which has been adapted from models for the growing sport of 'hang gliding' with 16 to 25 ft. span Flex Wings.

AUTOGYROS

Another type of aircraft that has a suspended fuselage is the Autogyro. Here, the rotor blades 'windmill' and offer a cone of lift as the blades rotate. For models, the blades which are normally three in number for ease of balance and construction, are like small wings. They are set at a negative angle to the rotor shaft, in order to blow around when the model is held into wind for the launch. Because the angle of the shaft is swept back, the rotor disc as a whole presents itself at a positive angle to the airstream and so the Autogyro gains lift. Inherent difficulties are that the rotor blades must never be allowed to stall and this can happen if in an over-anxious launch, the model is thrown forwards. Autogyros should always be allowed to lift themselves off from a launch. The balance should be just aft of the rotor shaft. It may be necessary to employ an 'upside' down tail with an inverted airfoil section in some cases, and considerable engine downthrust which aids the rotor through slipstream effect. When power ceases, the rotor continues in the same direction and the auto-rotation produces a safe and slow descent.

One can have twin or even triple rotors on a model, or, to eliminate the torque effect on the single rotor, can use opposite rotation of twin rotors mounted with appropriate safe spacing on a single shaft, one above the other. No tail rotor is needed, and the fuselage can be an old free-flight model body, converted.

HELICOPTERS

One of the simplest indoor flying machines is a helicopter made with four feathers, two corks, a rubber band and a short length of stick. The feathers are stuck by their quills into the corks to make miniature propellers with feather blades at about 20 deg. angles. One cork is pierced and fixed to the stick 'shaft', the other has a paper clip wire bent as a hook and attached to run in a bearing at the opposite end of the 'shaft'. Connect the hook with a point at the end of other shaft end by means of the rubber band so that when the 'propeller' is wound up, the rubber motor will then drive it back again. Ensure that 'propellers' are so twisted to screw in opposite directions, wind up the rubber band and release the device. It will helicopter in the room and hover under the ceiling. Main distinction of the helicopter is that the rotor is driven and only free-wheels in the gliding descent when power ceases. While the rotor is being driven, the blades are at a positive angle. With developed modern models, the blades change to a negative angle for the auto-rotation needed on descent.

All manner of drives is possible, except for a true scale replica of the full-size system where an engine in the fuselage drives the rotor shaft through a clutch. Models have been constructed with miniature clutches but the additional weight, lower efficiency and engine cooling problems make it a task only for the ardent scale purist. Instead, the rotor is usually driven by *reaction* or *direct thrust*.

The reaction drive is simplest. An engine is fitted to the centre of the rotor, complete with tank, and facing upwards so that the small propeller on the engine can be accessible for starting. The propeller is mounted in a gimbal. In other words, it can 'seesaw' so that though the engine and rotor can swing, the prop. disc will be stabilized and act as a powerful corrective force. Since the engine prop. will be travelling anti-clockwise, then the crankcase and the rotor hub to which it is attached will want to travel in the opposite, clockwise, rotation through torque *reaction*. While the engine screams at 10,000 revolutions per minute, the torque-driven rotor chops around at about 600 r.p.m. and up goes the helicopter!

The direct thrust method is also simple in that there is a mounting bar at right angles to a two-blade rotor, on which are the two engines or one engine and a blob of lead to balance. These engines drive thrust airscrews at right angles to the rotor movement, in other words they pull the rotor blades around. This is quite simple and it is extraordinary what weight can be carried by two small engines driving a very large rotor. The mass weight of the rotating engines presents a little gyroscopic difficulty; but though flight may not be as smooth as the real thing, the direct drive gives little fuel feed trouble and is very easy to make.

The most spectacular development of the early 70s was the radio controlled helicopter as pioneered by Ing. Dieter Schlüter of Frankfurt. Kit sets, costing £150 plus are sold for at least five different R/C helicopters, some with full cyclic pitch controls.

One other rotary wing machine deserves mention. It is the single-blade helicopter which Charles McCutcheon, an American student at Cambridge University, created when he sought the simplest ever type of flying machine. It is a single blade, with extended shaft on which is mounted a direct thrust motor as just described. At right angles to the blade, one fits an arm with a balance weight which controls rate of climb, and on the rotor blade tip there is a small 'tail' set at negative angle to induce a positive angle on the blade. This machine has been copied throughout the world, labelled a Russian, Czech, or Polish invention, but remains the 'McCutcheon Flying Machine' and is a fascinator in all languages.

CHAPTER 9

Competitions

The spirit of competitive aeromodelling, of matching one's own efforts against those of other modellers, is a most important factor in the well-being of the modern model movement. Chapter 1 detailed the many categories for which both National and International contests are held. In general they are for duration, speed or judgement of aerobatic ability according to the kind of model.

The National organization in Great Britain is in the hands of the *Society of Model Aeronautical Engineers Ltd.*, a voluntary Council of Officials being served by a paid secretary to administer, and a nation-wide system of Area Sub-Committees and Technical Sub-Committees supplying the Council with recommendations and resolutions. The process is most democratic. If an individual member wishes to raise any matter, he does so through his club secretary to the local Area, the country being divided into seventeen such Areas. The matter is tabled at the next Area Committee meeting, and if they cannot deal effectively, their Area Delegate, serving as spokesman for that section of the country, is directed to support any discussion on the matter when it is tabled before the Council of Officers.

Should the matter be of a technical nature, then the appropriate sub-committee is asked to provide its opinion. These sub-committees consist of up to five experts in the category, and they also guide any contest rule changes that may be deemed necessary in the light of progress.

When a National contest is held (and there are many, from March to October each year) it can be either *Decentralized* (run at local club grounds with all flights certified by club officials and returned to the S.M.A.E. Ltd. Competition Secretary); *Centralized* (all competitors use the same flying field, where an appointed or voluntary organization officiates); or *Area-centralized* (where all competitors within an Area gather at one flying field and the Area officials are administrators).

The Annual National Championships, usually held at Whitsun at a fairly central venue (Royal Air Force Station, Hullavington and Lindholme have been used mostly) is the largest of the events and attracts a great camping community with much stimulating activity. It is the highlight of the year, early enough to inspire many modellers to new ideas for the rest of the season, and near enough to peak daylight hours to ensure a very long week-end of aeromodelling. To the visitor it is very much a Jamboree with little apparent organization, due to the fact that most events are run from small control points and there are many such events going on simultaneously over the length and breadth of the airfield. However, everyone has tremendous enjoyment at the annual 'Nats' and it is not to be missed.

National contests are run to slightly different rules to those used Internationally. Whereas the International body (F.A.I.) has strict specifications for the free-flight classes, the British contests are also for unrestricted specification models as well as those to F.A.I. specifications; and so encouragement is given to the person who has no wish to build a model of specific weight, area, power, etc.

Similarly, flight durations are extended for the rubber-driven class so that a 'maximum' flight time here is 4 min. whereas in all other classes, including the F.A.I. events, it is 3 min. That is to say, all duration over 3 min. does not count. Obviously, a model will be trimmed for absolute duration and a tail tipping device or parachute brought into action to bring the model down as soon as possible after the 'maximum' has elapsed. Object of the limit is to contain the contest within the precincts of the average aerodrome. In usual British weather conditions, with winds gusting to 15 m.p.h., the maximum flights usually land very close or outside the perimeter.

In National contests, three flights are allowed, and in the event of a modeller making a perfect score of three maxima, he and others then make a fourth flight which is unlimited and timed to conclusion. This decides the individual placing. In International contests to the F.A.I. regulations, the event is for a total of seven flights and in the case of a perfect score, then succeeding flights are made, each with the increment of 60 sec. added to the previous maximum. Thus the eighth round becomes 4 min., the ninth for 5 min., the tenth for 6 min., etc. The winner will be the highest individual score at the stage where either one or no competitor achieves the set maximum.

COMPETITIONS

In F.A.I. Free Flight Power duration contests the eighth flight is
with 8 seconds engine run instead of 10 seconds and the ninth with
6 secs; the tenth and subsequent with only 4 secs.

AEROBATICS

In these classes we have a standardization, for the International
and National aerobatic schedules are identical. Each is set a schedule
of manœuvres through which the radio controller or control-line
'pilot' must send his model. Points are awarded by a panel of judges
for the shape and smoothness of the manœuvre and the schedule is so
designed as to extract the greatest possible display of control exerted
by the operator. The most difficult item to execute in the radio-control schedule is the pure stall or 'Tail slide'. The model is expected to

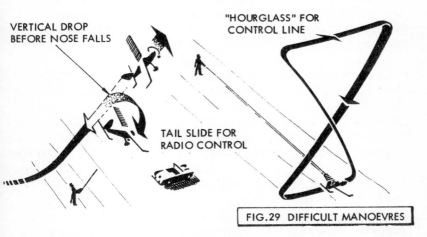

VERTICAL DROP
BEFORE NOSE FALLS

"HOURGLASS" FOR
CONTROL LINE

TAIL SLIDE FOR
RADIO CONTROL

FIG. 29 DIFFICULT MANOEVRES

climb, then, with the nose still pointing up, the power is to be cut off
until no forward speed exists, the model loses inertia and lift then
slides back on the climbing track. It calls for rudder, aileron, engine
and elevator control! Among the control-line manœuvres, the 'Hourglass' figure is most difficult. This requires the model to turn from a
straight line climb or dive (of past the vertical angle) through 120
deg. at only 5 ft. radius of turn, into horizontal flight. Turns are close
together, and because of the hemisphere in which the control-line
model is obliged to operate, the 'hourglass' calls for very fast pilot
action (Fig. 29).

COMPETITIONS

Other manœuvres are developments of the loop in upright and inverted planes. The vertical, horizontal and overhead eights are typical. For control-line there are added 'square' variations. In either case, emphasis in points is made on the quality of landing for this is by no means an easy concluding item.

Judges assess each manœuvre on a 0–10 basis, then each item is given a 'K' factor according to the difficulty of execution. Level flight gains a small 'K' factor and the Hourglass or Tail slide will have a high factor. By multiplying the judge's pointage by the factor, the distinction between good and indifferent flight qualities is magnified. Five judges are used in International events and the highest and lowest discarded, leaving an 'average' result. Since the whole contest thus hinges on personal opinion of the manœuvre quality, there is always argument on the validity of the judge's ruling, for inevitably, when dealing with the varied characteristics and temperaments of many nations, even five judges cannot hope to satisfy the opinions of everyone!

SCALE MODELS

A similar situation occurs with the three categories (control line, free flight and radio control) of scale model judging, except that there is further division of opinion on which type of model, modern or veteran, deserves special consideration. An answer to this is provided by the S.M.A.E. rules which break the aeroplane down into some fourteen components each of which is judged separately, and which are so arranged to give almost all kinds of subject an even opportunity. However, models are not subjected to scale judging until *after* they have proved that they can fly over a minimum distance, or duration, or through a flight pattern that is also judged for points. Thus it will be seen that competitive scale aeromodelling is a most exacting process, and the winner is always quite an exceptional example of the hobby.

CONCOURS D'ELEGANCE

Sometimes there will be a 'beauty' event at a model rally, laid on as a crowd pleaser and static exhibition as distinct from the activity on the flying field. Here we find the superbly polished models competing in 'Concours d'Elégance' where no flight has to be made and all the judging is based solely on the workmanship. It is quite a popular

event and attracts good support for there are many modern aeromodellers who have no wish other than to work hard at construction
and then fly very occasionally. Museum finishes and fine detail work
are to be admired just as much as flying ability. This contest gives an
opportunity to the otherwise hidden talents of the fastidious constructor.

Beside Rat racing, which was mentioned in Chapter 5, there is
another flying event which is aimed at the general or 'sports' flyer.
This is the free flight Scramble. All entries are lined up, with a time-
keeper allocated to each entrant. At a signal, all models are launched.
Flights of less than 20 sec. do not count, nor do those of over 2 min.
The competitor makes as many flights as he can within the half or
full hour period set, and the winner is the one with highest gross
duration over his flights. There is no more exhausting a contest, nor
one so thrilling as the sight of the first launch! All manner of models
are flown in this event, from the hand-launched 'chuck' glider to the
helicopter. It calls for something tough and easy to operate. It should
not drift far, and it should fly for as near as possible 2 min. at each
launching. Anyone amassing more than a 20-min. total within the
hour has (a) a good model and (b) splendid physical condition!

It is this sort of contest that serves the club well. Parents can time-
keep while all the club takes part on the local field. An aerodrome is
not necessary and the time limits should be set according to local
conditions.

Other ideal primary contests are for the smaller model specifications, the A/1 glider class, or the Coupe d'Hiver. These are models of
about 40 in. span, easy to handle and to fly, and created for smaller
field flying. Many kit and plan designs meet the simple specifications
and in particular, the A/1 glider class is frequently used as a subject
for club 'one-design' class events, all modellers flying the same
model type. This way there is a good direct comparison of building
standards and flight trim. Much can be learned from such practical
comparison.

This is the best way to get started in competition flying. Then as
the bug begins to bite, enthusiasm for contests knows few bounds.
The chase for new techniques, design trends and latest materials is a
constant stimulant.

COMPETITIONS

RALLIES

Apart from the many contests which are organized by the S.M.A.E. during the season from March to October, there are many Rallies, Gala days and model meetings which are run by areas and clubs to maintain enthusiasm and give people a chance of gathering at one venue for a picnic style meeting as distinct from the tough and purposeful National contest. Rallies are usually an outing for the family. During òne North-Western Area rally at the A. V. Roe airfield, Woodford, in Cheshire, there were more than 9,000 spectators and participants on the airfield. Less than 200 of these people would have been directly engaged in the contests. The rest were there to fly for fun, to watch and enjoy the atmosphere. Such Rallies keep the movement together.

Competitors are awarded prizes in cash or kind plus a silver trophy which is retained for a year, engraved, then passed to the next winner. Prizes in kind are preferable, they hold the sporting atmosphere and are more satisfactory from all points of view.

RECORDS

25¾ *hours* duration flying on a slope, 260 miles in a straight line, 210 miles per hour speed. These are by no means unrealistic records currently within the scope of the modern model. The International body, F.A.I., promulgates records in the duration, distance, altitude and speed categories for most classes of model. Such a record must be observed by officials and be certified by the National Aero Club.

British records are set annually. That is to say, a record for the year can be claimed but it will not be carried on to the next year. Again, an official in the club must certify the flight and claim.

Anyone with an inclination for contest flying should belong to a model club, and can obtain the address of the local secretary on application to the S.M.A.E. or the modelling magazines.

------------------------◎------------------------

CHAPTER 10

Construction Techniques

------------------------◎------------------------

The structure of a modern model aeroplane is a blend which produces *shape, section* and adequate *strength*. The applications are numerous. One can use the well-known system of building up with small section balsa strips, or make the components of sheet balsa, or use modern plastics such as expanded polystyrene, or have a mixed structure of these systems.

Everything depends upon the purpose of the model. If it is to be a competition type, then structure weight should be as light as permissible for the strength and power needed. If made for sport flying, the model can be made specially tough with no concessions to weight and the engine size adjusted according to the final weight. Most sport designs accept a range of power, for example, from ·75 c.c. up to 1·5 c.c., or 2·5 c.c. to 5 c.c. and are thus flexible in choice of engine and propeller.

Another consideration that is given less attention in modern aero-modelling than before, is that of streamlining. There was a time when the squared tip shape on wings and tail was abhorred, when anything but an elliptical cross section fuselage was thought a lazy approach, and when sheet surfaces were considered hopelessly inefficient.

As long as the model does not present an absolute 'blank wall' to the airstream and the components are reasonably well finished, stream-lining has little importance *except* in cases where absolute efficiency is demanded (in speed, team racing, aerobatic events). Rectangular cross sections are adequate for sport model fuselages, either free flight or control-line.

FUSELAGES

The well-established box type fuselage, made of four longerons with vertical and horizontal spacers from square section balsa is light and, once covered, quite strong. It forms a fuselage in itself, or can be the centre box with surrounding formers mounted upon it

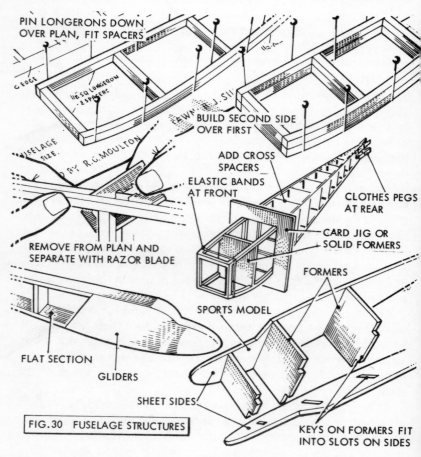

PIN LONGERONS DOWN OVER PLAN, FIT SPACERS

C EDGE

1/16 SQ LONGERON 2 SPACERS

BUILD SECOND SIDE OVER FIRST

FUSELAGE SIZE.

BY R.G. MOULTON

ADD CROSS SPACERS

ELASTIC BANDS AT FRONT

CLOTHES PEGS AT REAR

REMOVE FROM PLAN AND SEPARATE WITH RAZOR BLADE

CARD JIG OR SOLID FORMERS

FORMERS

SPORTS MODEL

FLAT SECTION

GLIDERS

SHEET SIDES

FIG. 30 FUSELAGE STRUCTURES

KEYS ON FORMERS FIT INTO SLOTS ON SIDES

to give a curved shape which is followed by stringers or planking. To make the basic box we use pins to locate the upper and lower longerons over the plan. Upright spacers are cemented in place, then the second side is built directly over the top of the first to ensure identical shape. Longerons should have first been selected as pairs with near equal bending resistance.

When sides are made and separated, they are joined by the cross spacers, using a card jig to hold the body square. Sometimes a permanent balsa former is incorporated and this will hold the squareness of the fuselage shape at the maximum cross section. Subsidiary formers are added, longeron end points joined laterally and the structure filled in.

This type of structure is limited to the rubber-driven model in the main (Fig. 30). Glider fuselages are sheeted over a spruce or flat section ($\frac{1}{8} \times \frac{1}{2}$ in.) longeron which offers a slim fuselage of low drag. Sport model fuselages are from slabs of sheet balsa with strengthenings at appropriate points to take landing and handling wear. They are assembled with formers and bulkeads which have small tongues projecting into the sheet sides through slots. If longerons are fitted, they offer the advantage that corners can be sandpapered off to a round section as there will be more body in the corner joints (Fig. 30).

A development of the sheet side, with special consideration for strength and weight saving is to be found in radio-controlled models. Here the sides are of relatively thin sheet for the model size ($\frac{1}{16}$ in. sheet on a 54 in. span model) and just as with the basic box fuselage,

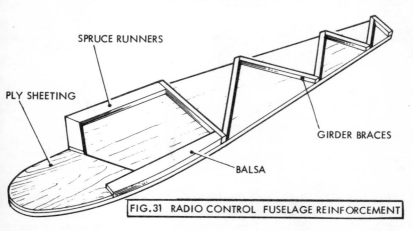

SPRUCE RUNNERS

PLY SHEETING

GIRDER BRACES

BALSA

FIG. 31 RADIO CONTROL FUSELAGE REINFORCEMENT

a structure is built up, over the sheet side. Additional sheeting is cross grained on top and the result is a very strong unit. Soft balsa should always be selected.

111

Block balsa is a good but rather expensive medium for shapes which are otherwise difficult to plank or obtain with stringers and covering. Any large blocks should be hollowed after the outside shape is perfected.

Plywood linings or 'doublers' for the nose section of a radio-controlled or control-line fuselage are to be recommended. This part of the model is usually the most highly stressed, especially in an un-wanted crash, and a little extra effort in the construction often pays great dividends (Fig. 31).

Scale model shapes are frequently elliptical. The only means of obtaining such a cross section in wood (apart from a hollowed block) is to plank over shaped formers. The fuselage is made by laying down a vertical or horizontal crutch over the plan which will serve to hold the correct taper, etc. Half formers are fitted, then a master stringer. When one side is assembled with the main stringer on the formers, the construction is lifted off the plan and other half formers added together with another master stringer. Now that the basic shape is formed, strips of planking can be laid over, working symmetrically in order that no bias is pulled into the frame to twist the shape of the fuselage (Fig. 32). Alternatively, the planking could be replaced by

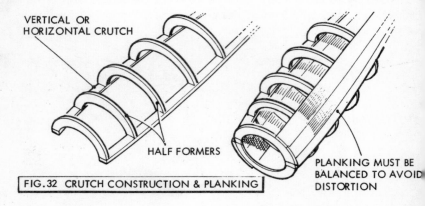

VERTICAL OR HORIZONTAL CRUTCH

HALF FORMERS

PLANKING MUST BE BALANCED TO AVOID DISTORTION

FIG. 32 CRUTCH CONSTRUCTION & PLANKING

balsa stringers with covering to hold the shape. This has special value on a scale type where stringers and fabric are to be represented. If the stringers are of rectangular section ($\frac{1}{16} \times \frac{1}{8}$ in.) and set on edge they will have better strength contribution and also resistance to sag as the covering is tautened by dope.

Sometimes the crutch system is not possible on a scale type due to

13. Beautifully constructed radio-control scale model of the Cessna 172 for single-channel operation using rudder only. This model weighs over 6 lb. and makes long exciting take-offs with its moderate 3·5 c.c. power

14. Dummy engines on this Caproni bomber hide two 6 c.c. model engines. Very fine detail including the steerable pair of nose wheels makes this an outstanding model in the Milani collection. Now donated to the Imperial War Museum, London

15. This radio-controlled model of a Messerschmitt Me 163 Rocket Fighter was the World Championship winner of 1972 in the contest held at Toulouse, France. The designer, Heinz Simon of West Germany uses a radio-controlled tractor to tow the 70 in. model into position. He fits the flying airscrew to the engine in the nose, and the model takes off, as does the real machine, from a dolly

16. Kurt Saupe of Switzerland flying his radio-controlled scale model 'Gazelle' helicopter in hover at the first Domenico Agusta trophy contest held near Milan in 1973. The model is entirely Kurt's design and it can simulate the real machine in all aspects

large cabin areas interfering and preventing such structure in parts which ought to be transparent. In this case, the fuselage can be assembled over a central stick jig 'Kebab' style like the sweetmeats on a skewer. All formers and bulkheads have a hole through which the stick will tightly pass. If open frame formers are wanted, then temporary centres can be fitted for the initial assembly.

PLASTICS

Modern aeromodelling is very much up to date with latest techniques as devised for industrial use and Glass Fibre has been employed for model fuselages for several years. Team racers, speed models and small radio-control types have a special call for the kind of strength offered by Glass Fibre.

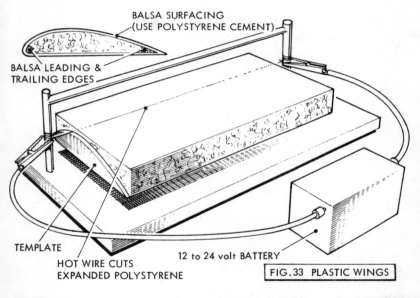

FIG.33 PLASTIC WINGS

Simplest method is to make a balsa shape, slightly undersize, then make up the Glass Fibre body over it and fill the rough surface to make it presentable. This is heavy and not always satisfactory for the enthusiast who wants a metallic surface. For him, the 'female' mould is best. Make the balsa shape to exact size, cast a plaster 'female' of it, then mould the Glass Fibre body on the *inside* of the plaster. The result needs no filler and is very smooth.

Simoniz wax should be rubbed into the mould as well as a release agent on top, then one 'gel coat' of resin is brushed on, then a layer of ·009 in. cloth, more resin and more cloth in spots where thickness and strength are called for. Allow to cure properly, then take out of the mould which can be used repeatedly.

Another plastic which is being used increasingly is Expanded Polystyrene. This is a white foam-like plastic composed of irregular-shaped cells, fused together. It is non-porous but not easy to surface, and it calls for special adhesives. The plastic can be cut with ease, using either a hot wire (to be preferred) or balsa knife, and as it weighs only 3 lb. per cu. ft., it can be used in large blocks for a model. Since it possesses little tensile or compression strength it needs longerons for a fuselage or spars for a wing. These can be inserted into grooves cut in the shapes and a balsa outer sheeting completes an adequate structure. Wing sections are shaped from solid E/Polystyrene by the hot wire method (thin wire short-circuited by about 12 volts) whereby the wire is stretched across two templates and cuts through the plastic like butter (Fig. 33). An entire model can be made in E/Polystyrene but if it is a power model, as we pointed out in Chapter 2, protection must be given to the structure against the solvent action of model engine fuels. Covering with a layer of tissue coated with cellulose fillers is a good protective. Handling the E/Polystyrene model is not altogether easy, for due to the softness, the material will dent. However, in our experience, it resumes shape if the area dented is dampened.

WINGS

Ribs are eliminated if a solid E/Polystyrene shape is to be used. They are, in the case of a tapered wing, the hardest item to fabricate and certainly the most important. Aerofoil shape should always be maintained as designed. Deviation will change the flight characteristics and not always for the better!

Use a master template, cut from ply or aluminium, and duplicate or make one to represent the root and another for the tip ribs. Then shape the rib profiles by the 'sandwich' method where rectangles of balsa are sandwiched between the templates and shaped to the profiles. If there is to be any taper, then by arrangement of the root and tip ribs at their respective relationship, the taper comes automatically (Fig. 34).

CONSTRUCTION TECHNIQUES

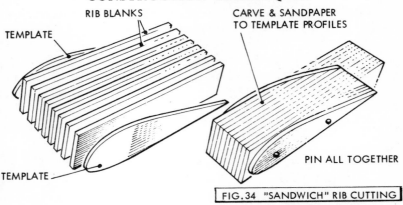

FIG.34 "SANDWICH" RIB CUTTING

Wing structure can be as varied as with fuselages. The critical factor is to retain the aerofoil section. This can only be done by sheeting the leading edge on top and bottom surfaces back to about 40 per cent of the wing chord; but this is not always possible. The alternative, weight-saving system, is to have multiple wing spars all on the wing surface so that the tissue or cloth covering adopts a series of straight lines between covering supports. Not to have spars will mean that the inevitable sag between ribs on covering will reduce the effective wing thickness. This is not so bad as long as due allowance is made by making the ribs deeper than originally intended (Fig. 35).

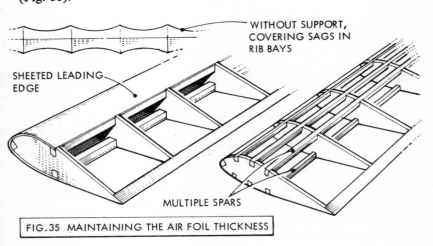

FIG.35 MAINTAINING THE AIR FOIL THICKNESS

CONSTRUCTION TECHNIQUES

Warps are the enemy and in order to alleviate the situation, one can employ the diagonal rib bracing favoured by competition enthusiasts. Often, only that part of the rib aft of the mainspar is set diagonally, since it is this area which warps, but sometimes we see 'egg-box' construction with ribs overlapped and at about 60 deg. to leading and trailing edge (Fig. 36).

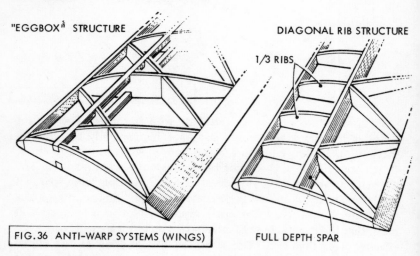

"EGGBOX" STRUCTURE

DIAGONAL RIB STRUCTURE

1/3 RIBS

FIG.36 ANTI-WARP SYSTEMS (WINGS)

FULL DEPTH SPAR

Even the best of designed anti-warp structures fails in its purpose if the covering is allowed to apply concentrations of stress at weaker points, and so it is firmly the view of the author that standard structures (with sheeted leading edges and 'straight' ribs) are ideal for wings and that greater emphasis should be laid upon the application of the covering and the *flatness of the building board*. The last point is the most important of all!

TAILS

All that has been said for the wing will also stand for the horizontal stabilizer, which we call the tailplane, and also the fin and rudder. However, the tail surfaces may be flat and not of lifting aerofoil section. When so thin, they are warp prone and being in effect control surfaces on all kinds of model this is very important.

A flat tail surface can be made of balsa sheet if soft wood is used and the model will accept the weight (has a long enough nose to balance without call for ballast) and the size is compatible with soft balsa available. BUT, if a sheet surface is used and the natural span-wise grain direction employed, then rectangular inserts of harder grade balsa MUST be fitted at key points in order to stop the sheet from curling. Even the best prepared sheet tail from the most expert modeller's workshop will curl from the flat if exposed to heat on a summer's day, and may curve in the opposite direction in winter if no inserts are used.

Similarly, the built-up structure of flat section will warp to a lesser degree but this can easily be controlled by application of balsa sheeting on one surface. For example a $\frac{3}{8} \times \frac{1}{8}$ in. frame for a 15-in. span tail can be covered on *one* side with soft balsa sheet, and then tissue or cloth covered all over will be lighter than an all-sheet balsa equivalent (Fig. 37).

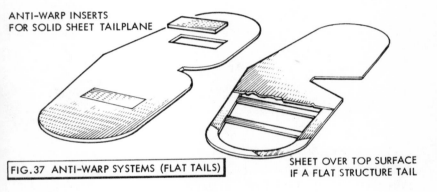

ANTI-WARP INSERTS
FOR SOLID SHEET TAILPLANE

SHEET OVER TOP SURFACE
IF A FLAT STRUCTURE TAIL

FIG.37 ANTI-WARP SYSTEMS (FLAT TAILS)

JOINTS

Always try to have the ribs into the trailing edges of wing and tail by at least $\frac{1}{8}$ in. This is a great strength and anti-warp aid. Set leading edges diagonally in Vee cuts at nose ribs for better alignment and to obtain an easy surface on which to adhere the leading edge sheeting. Use a slow drying (P.V.A.) or impact adhesive for leading edge sheeting. Do not cut into spars unless absolutely necessary. Fit plywood dihedral keepers at the wing root but not at the outer dihedral break. This allows a tip to break away in a crash without it ripping the spars apart in the centre panel. Ply joiners are *not* required at outer wing joints; a butt joint, with gussets at the rib to spar joints, is ample.

CONSTRUCTION TECHNIQUES

MODEL ASSEMBLY

Even the most ideal structures fall down if they are incorrectly assembled as a whole unit. Make the wing and tail unit *key* to their respective positions so that on each assembly, they can be fitted *exactly as previously tested* (Fig. 38). Have the rubber band dowels so

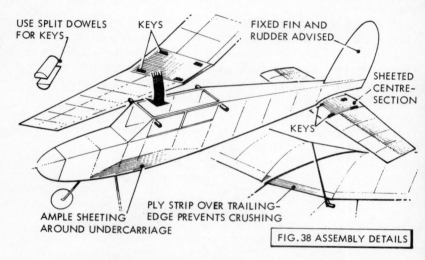

USE SPLIT DOWELS FOR KEYS

KEYS

FIXED FIN AND RUDDER ADVISED

SHEETED CENTRE-SECTION

KEYS

AMPLE SHEETING AROUND UNDERCARRIAGE

PLY STRIP OVER TRAILING-EDGE PREVENTS CRUSHING

FIG. 38 ASSEMBLY DETAILS

positioned that the bands do not try to pull the surface from its true position. Also arrange the dowels so that the surfaces can quickly detach in a crash. The rubber bands are tough too, so always protect the tapered trailing edge with a ply facing on top to avoid unnecessary damage. Undercarriages create havoc if wrenched out of place in a hard landing. Make sure that the area around the undercarriage is sheeted, using thin ply for the Dural sheet U/C type. Try always to allow for the worst to happen!

CHAPTER 11

---◎---

Covering and Finishing

---◎---

Many aeromodellers take such pride in the final appearance of their efforts that the coloured finish and decoration becomes the longest and certainly most involved section of the construction. There are so many methods available to the modern aeromodeller that it is first advisable for us to examine the requirements according to the type of model.

Simplest is the duration type, where, as we have pointed out, weight is an important factor and the modeller cannot afford lavish decoration. Here, we use *coloured tissue* as a covering and decorative medium.

Next, the sport model with an engine, for free flight or control line. This should be tough, and can be covered with tissue and colour doped, or *coloured fabric.*

Then the scale model, which needs to be robust and can be fabric, with scale colours doped on, plus *grain fillers and dope* over the areas which are sheeted.

Finally, the indoor flyer which will have *unprepared tissue* or *microfilm* as a covering medium. Also the newly discovered coverings for models which are *plastics.*

TISSUE

The lightest grade of model covering for outdoor use is Japanese hand-made tissue. It was once known as 'Rice' paper when an American was specially gifted with imagination in producing advertising copy but in fact it owes its origin to wood pulp just like most other papers. It comes plain, white, or coloured, has a definite grain which allows the tissue to pull more one way than the other and it

119

COVERING AND FINISHING

fills easily on one application of shrinking dope. A British paper known as 'Modelspan' has a similar structure but is not grain directional. It is of heavier grade in lightest form, and much heavier grade in its 'heavy' form but it is tougher and will not shatter on impact. A full range of colours is available and like the 'bamboo' paper development of the Jap tissue, can be bought in 'wet-strengthened' state. This means it can be dampened and will not break up whilst being handled for covering a frame. Thus the tissue can be applied while damp, a great advantage where compound curves are present or there is a tendency for wrinkles to appear. Wet tissue can be stretched as it is applied.

The best manner of application for all forms of tissue covering is not the simplest (Fig. 39). First apply thick grade clear dope to all

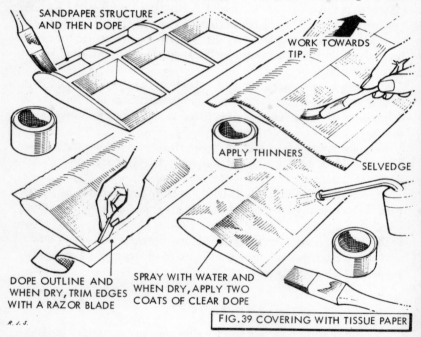

SANDPAPER STRUCTURE AND THEN DOPE

WORK TOWARDS TIP.

APPLY THINNERS

SELVEDGE

DOPE OUTLINE AND WHEN DRY, TRIM EDGES WITH A RAZOR BLADE

SPRAY WITH WATER AND WHEN DRY, APPLY TWO COATS OF CLEAR DOPE

FIG.39 COVERING WITH TISSUE PAPER

the edges where tissue is to be adhered. Allow to dry then apply tissue over the frame, and brush dope thinners over the pre-doped areas, *through* the tissue. This dissolves the dope surface and holds the tissue as laid over. Keep the tissue wrinkle free (if need be, iron between sheets of newspaper to flatten) and if Jap tissue is used, keep

120

the selvedge parallel to the wing ribs in order to have the tissue grain aid covering. This way, the sag between ribs is minimized. Pull covering taut as possible before adhering to the framework so that sag is reduced, this for all forms of covering.

If the tissue had been wet on application, it should be allowed to dry. Where the dope is 'blushed' with whiteness, a quick application of more thinners will clear the spot up after due time is allowed for thorough drying out. If the tissue has been applied dry, now spray lightly with water so that the entire surface is just damp. A scent spray or even a flick from a nail brush will suffice for the water application. As the tissue dries, so will it shrink to the desired shape. There is an appreciable amount of shrinkage and thin structures should always be pinned to a flat surface as one side is treated and dried at a time. Otherwise a warp will develop.

Easiest method of tissue application is by use of photographic mounting paste. This is smeared over the framework areas bay by bay and the tissue stuck down, working from root to tip. It is not as neat as the doping system, nor so permanent for undersurfaces where the tissue has to follow concave shapes against the undercamber of wing ribs; but it is good enough and ample for 90 per cent of models.

Always rub the tissue down with the finger-tips to ensure good adhesion, and when fully shrunk by water, apply a coat of dope to all the framework contact points through the tissue. This doubly secures the 'joint' and also helps fill the tissue pores so that the final finish will be even all over.

As the tissue will be applied over wing half panels, or fuselage sides, there must inevitably be an excess overlap of about 1 in. minimum all round. This should be trimmed after the drying out stage, and a sharp razor-blade employed. Leave an $\frac{1}{8}$ in. strip to wrap round and overlap edges or an ugly plain wood line appears as an irregular eyesore. Cover undersurfaces first, then top sides.

The first coat of clear shrinking dope should be sparingly applied. Many light applications are far superior to one heavy swamping and if a few drops of castor oil are added to a half-pint can of clear dope as a 'plasticiser' then the result of many coats of dope will be further improved with a resistance to shattering.

Sometimes a *double* covering of tissue is a benefit (Fig. 40). If Jap tissue is used, then the grain directions should be set at right angles to one another with the lower layer having the selvedge in line with the ribs, and the top layer having the selvedge along trailing or leading

121

edge. Apply one thin coat of dope to the lower layer before the other tissue is laid over and doped to the outline as before. Then the upper surface will slide over the doped lower layer as it becomes taut.

Tissue which can be applied wet should not be wrung out in a ball; but kept flat and dipped in a large pan of water then hung to drain off the excess. A towel or sheets of blotting paper can be used as absorbents for excess water, the tissue being laid over them to dry off a little.

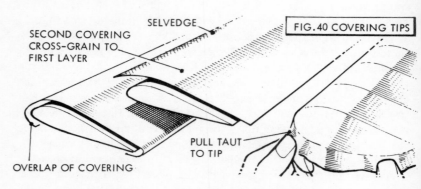

SELVEDGE

SECOND COVERING CROSS-GRAIN TO FIRST LAYER

FIG. 40 COVERING TIPS

PULL TAUT TO TIP

OVERLAP OF COVERING

If the model is to have a final finish of fuel-proof dope from the range of *Butyrate* finishes, then one should start off with Butyrate instead of cellulose clear shrinking dope. In fact it pays to stay with one type of dope, even one make of dope right through the whole process.

Three or four coats of clear dope are usually enough to seal the pores of tissue. The purpose is to make the surface air and watertight. A ready check is to suck at a wing and if air is noticeably drawn through, then another coat of dope is advised. As a final sealer and weatherproofer, a coat of clear varnish (cellulose) or non-shrink finish known as 'Banana oil' gives a good effect. Alternatively, if colouring is wanted the bootmaker's aniline dye (suspended in methylated spirits) will give rich translucent colouring. Some modellers decorate with strips of different coloured tissues which are doped in place, even running to the extent of having numerals and letters cut from tissue. The effect is most pleasing and the weight negligible.

COVERING AND FINISHING

FABRIC

The larger model should be covered with a fabric and either left in natural colour as a weight saver for the duration model or doped with colours for other types. We can use Silk, Nylon, Terylene and other man-made fibres. Nylon is the strongest, Terylene has strong resistance to shrinkage and is therefore more difficult to apply, while silk is lightest and easiest to apply.

The procedure is identical to that described for covering with tissue, especially wet tissue, for all of the fabrics should be applied wet. Since Nylon does not shrink at a rate anywhere near that of tissue or silk, it must be applied as taut as possible in the first instance. It also tends to be of an open weave and a mixture of talcum powder with the adhesive dope and thinners will be helpful in sealing the pores over the framework contact areas.

Cut an ample overlap for the panel, soak the fabric, wring out the excess water and while it is drying, apply thick dope to the structure. Do not wait for it to dry fully before placing the fabric in place. Pin at the root rib, pull taut to the tip and pin there, then work out the wrinkles at the edges and without pulling too hard across the wing chord, make sure that the fabric is going to pull out smoothly. Then apply dope over the fabric-framework contact areas (Fig. 41).

With an open weave fabric there is a risk of the surface having pock marks at the contact areas. Also, the initial coat of dope tends to run through the fabric in parts and so create a heavily doped area, at the same time leaving a spot where holes are difficult to fill. Dust with talcum powder over the offending spot, then lightly dope. This is one remedy. A last desperate move in a bad case is to double cover with a bonding tissue over the top. A variation of this is to *start* with cheap open weave fabric and to allow for tissue bonding overlay for a finish. The wife or girl friend can usually oblige with old stockings that save the covering bill if used in this way.

Another point about fabric covering is that the warp and weft soon give away a badly stressed patch by showing the lines of thread in distortion instead of neat straight right angles. This is a great advantage at the covering stage. Always try not to get a stressed area that will be prone to a warp.

At least three coats of dope are needed to seal most fabrics. Silk in

COVERING AND FINISHING

special lightweight grade for model covering sometimes fills on a second coat but Nylon or the author's preference, Nylon Chiffon, takes at least three applications. If a spray is used, it may take even more to get the amount of shrinkage in Nylon. One can only rely on the contraction of the dope to tauten Nylon.

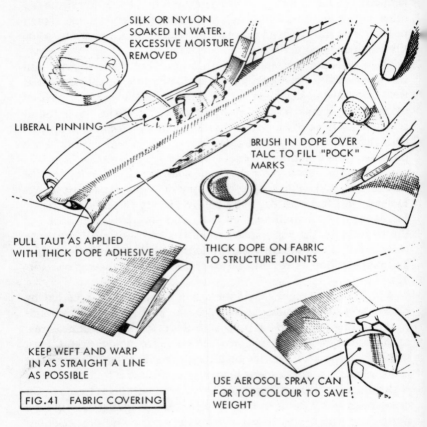

SILK OR NYLON SOAKED IN WATER. EXCESSIVE MOISTURE REMOVED

LIBERAL PINNING

BRUSH IN DOPE OVER TALC TO FILL "POCK" MARKS

PULL TAUT AS APPLIED WITH THICK DOPE ADHESIVE

THICK DOPE ON FABRIC TO STRUCTURE JOINTS

KEEP WEFT AND WARP IN AS STRAIGHT A LINE AS POSSIBLE

FIG.41   FABRIC COVERING

USE AEROSOL SPRAY CAN FOR TOP COLOUR TO SAVE WEIGHT

Where large areas of fabric-over-wood contacts are present, as for example on a sheeted wing leading edge, it pays to coat the surface with at least one application of sanding sealer as a filler, otherwise that section of the model is liable to take on a less well finished appearance than the plain fabric sections. A top coat of fuel proofer or varnish is the final 'leveller' to obtain an overall gloss.

124

COVERING AND FINISHING

GRAIN FILLERS

Very smooth and glossy finishes are expected on a wood surface and have particular advantage in a model where speed is the expectation. All the grain in the wood must be properly filled before the last coat of colour or natural varnish is applied. First sandpaper the unfinished wood as smooth as possible. Then give it a quick coat of dope to start the grain rising and the surface will be partially hardened in preparation for further sanding to take away the 'fuzz'. Now apply sanding sealer in three successive coats. Where grain is pitted and will not fill with sanding sealer, scrape Brummer stopper into the surface. Allow at least 24 hrs. to dry hard. Now sandpaper with what is known as 'wet or dry' paper. Start with a 300 grade, dip the paper in soapy water and rub with a circular motion. The paper should be frequently dipped so that it remains unclogged with erasures and this is the key to sanding success, for there will only be a scratch where the paper is allowed to carry a clogging. Rubbing should be concluded with successive finer grades of paper down to number 420 and the surface sighted against a light to detect smoothness. Almost all of the sealer should be removed.

One could then start to apply colour for a quick job and most British modellers spoil their work by slapping on top coats of colour at this stage instead of being patient.

Correct procedure is now to bond the surface to prevent the filler from cracking up under changes of temperature and humidity by doping a layer of Japanese tissue on the surface. More filler and rubbing follows. Now we have an excellent grounding for a metallic surface on wood. A coat of grey is best for a base coat, then several thin coats of the lightest of the final colours. White will never show satisfactorily over the top of the darker tones so this is the first to go on if used.

Spray painting is a great advantage, and the Aerosol cans, though initially expensive, can offer a superior finish with a fraction of bother and in far less time than is taken to dope. Coloured areas have to be masked carefully and here we can use Sellotape or the thinnest grade of Scotch Boy Drafting Tape to get the edges on curves, etc. However, the masking must either be removed immediately after dope application or after all is dry. To remove it whilst half dry is to tempt fate, for often the edge of the tape will tear off an area of the dope as a skin at this stage.

COVERING AND FINISHING

Use newspaper to shield the sections which must not be touched by the spray. It is cheap and will trim to awkward shapes.

Finally, a dose of 'elbow grease' with polishing will bring the lustre to the surface in a way one expects of the *Concours d'Elégance* model. Modern silicone polishes will bring a shine to most models that evokes admiration wherever displayed. They are, however, affected by some glowplug engine fuels, so any model likely to be sprayed by the exhaust of the engine or by siphoning from a fuel tank ventilator will be better protected with a liberal coating of fuel proofer.

PROOFERS

These can range from the 4-hr. drying Valspar synthetic clear varnish, applied over Valspar painted finishes, to the latest Epoxy resins. Most commercial proofers are of the latter type, with a hardener to add to the main resin just before the coat is applied. One must not exceed the quantity recommended for each of the makes, or the proofer will gel quickly and not spread. Some resins need to be heated slightly to thin down for easy brushing, so what may be a suspected case of dud stock, half dried, could well be some perfectly good proofer that needs a little warmth to bring it back to life. Excess hardener can create cracks and wrinkles in the colour, so be accurate in the mix.

MATT FINISHES

The most frequent question asked at model displays is, 'How can one obtain a scale *matt* finish on a wartime subject, that is fuel proof?'

One answer is to use a diesel engine and oil paints. It is in fact the only really satisfactory answer for any form of proofer imparts a gloss. This gloss can be cut back by rubbing over the proofer surface with 420 grade wet or dry paper and not polishing afterwards, or one can mix talc in the proofer which deadens the gloss but runs the risk of going lumpy on application.

The matt surfacing additives sold for oil paints for plastic kit models will have good apparent effect on small parts; but are still not proof against the glow fuel. In any case, the fuel and exhaust will themselves render a gloss on a matt surface, just as happened on full-size machines in wartime after some considerable Service use. The business of a perfect matt finish would only be absolutely accurate for a machine fresh from the factory production line.

126

PLASTICS

Modern aeromodelling is well abreast of industrial developments and every new item to appear in the factories is always seized upon by an enthusiast who spreads the word. Man-made rayon fibres as used for stiffening of ladies' apparel has been tried and after a spell of popularity, faded off. Various other grades of plastic sheeting, thin polythene and P.V.A. sheeting have also been tried but solvents for their adhesion and the weight consideration do not make them worthwhile. One material with promise is *Melinex* as made by Imperial Chemical Industries and used to cover the famous man-powered 'Puffin' and 'Jupiter'. This is a transparent film, sufficient in itself without any other protective or addition. It has to be adhered to a surface with an impact cement such as 'Evostik' and then shrunk as wanted by holding an ordinary household electric iron nearby. 'Mono Kote', 'Solarfilm' and 'Unicote' films are refined variations which have heat sealing adhesive incorporated and are now in all model shops. (Fig. 42.)

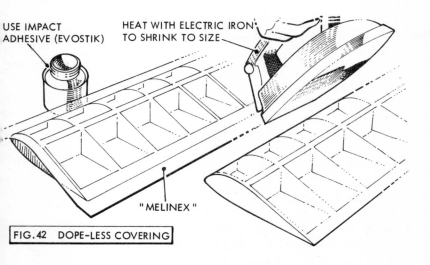

USE IMPACT ADHESIVE (EVOSTIK)

HEAT WITH ELECTRIC IRON TO SHRINK TO SIZE

" MELINEX "

FIG. 42   DOPE-LESS COVERING

INDOOR MODEL COVERING

As detailed in Chapter 2, Microfilm is the lightest known covering and is no more than a chemical deposit, spread on water then lifted as a film to apply to a thin frame (Fig. 43). It is not an expert's province and offers fascinating scope for experiment. A formula is quoted in the earlier reference and will give a good film for the novice.

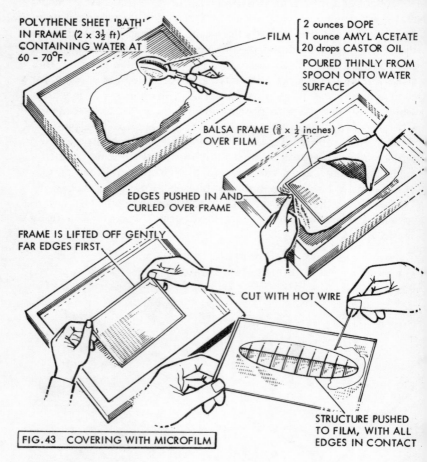

POLYTHENE SHEET 'BATH' IN FRAME (2 x 3½ ft) CONTAINING WATER AT 60 - 70°F.

FILM { 2 ounces DOPE
1 ounce AMYL ACETATE
20 drops CASTOR OIL

POURED THINLY FROM SPOON ONTO WATER SURFACE

BALSA FRAME (⅜ x ¼ inches) OVER FILM

EDGES PUSHED IN AND CURLED OVER FRAME

FRAME IS LIFTED OFF GENTLY FAR EDGES FIRST

CUT WITH HOT WIRE

STRUCTURE PUSHED TO FILM, WITH ALL EDGES IN CONTACT

FIG. 43 COVERING WITH MICROFILM

Other indoor models use tissue paper covering and here the ultra light grades of paper are essential. Japanese tissue can be too heavy! Instead, modellers employ *Condenser tissue* which is specially made for insulating of electrical condensers. It has a hard surface which does not need dope and is extraordinarily light for area. Application calls for care and thinned dope is the best adhesive.

CHAPTER 12

———————————◎———————————

Refinements, Hints and Tips

———————————◎———————————

There are numerous asides to modern aeromodelling apart from straightforward structural work and covering. Commercial bits and pieces are available to make a model more complete but quite often one has to make do with a nearly correct item when the absolutely right component could be home-made with a little extra trouble.

TRANSFERS

A first example is the decorative transfer. This can be for National, military or civil markings on a scale model, or one's own personal insignia on a sport model. Normal waterslide transfers are placed on the surface of lukewarm water so that the thick backing paper absorbs the water and this dissolves a glutinous layer on the rear face of the painted transfer. Once this is dissolved, the transfer floats away from the backing and the glutinous film sticks to the transfer and forms an adhesive. The transfer will slide into position on the model, all water is squeezed away from its under-surface and when dry, it is permanent.

Home-made transfers are applied in exactly the same manner. They are made on the gummed surface of a label, the gummier the better for this is the glutinous layer we have mentioned. Apply a coat of clear dope over the gum after adding a few drops of castor oil to the dope to provide flexibility. When the clear dope film is dry, draw the pattern to be painted on the surface and fill in with the various colour dopes as heavily and thickly as wanted. When all colour is painted on, allowed to dry and the home-made transfer ready for application, trim around with scissors, leaving about $\frac{1}{8}$ in. on the edge clear. The system works very well and has a wide range of applications.

I   129

PROPELLERS

Often one is obliged to carve a propeller in spite of there being a vast range on the model market. Special pusher types are made in only a few sizes, and a semi-scale blade shape or particular pitch may be required outside of the local shop stock. To carve a propeller is surprisingly easy and very satisfying so why not try it?

First process is to shape the blank. This means a squared off block which is profiled to the final plan and side elevations. The thickness of the blank depends upon the pitch of the propeller and this also determines the width. A very general rule for power model propellers is that the maximum width of the blades should be about 10 per cent of the diameter. Then, to obtain a pitch of 4 in., the blank should be $\frac{1}{4}$ in. thick; for 6 in. pitch, $\frac{3}{8}$ in. thick; for 8 in. pitch, $\frac{1}{2}$ in. thick and for higher pitches the blade angle and widths should be really carefully calculated.

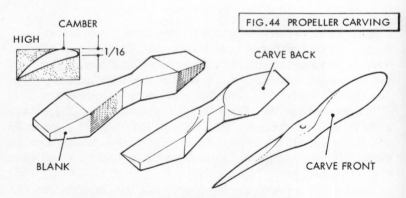

CAMBER

HIGH

1/16

BLANK

FIG. 44 PROPELLER CARVING

CARVE BACK

CARVE FRONT

On a rubber-driven propeller, the blade width is 15 per cent of diameter, and the maximum thickness about 10 per cent diameter, as the pitch of the rubber-driven model prop is usually 'square' or equal to diameter.

Carving the propeller is best executed with a whittling knife or broad chisel. The undersurfaces are always started first (Fig. 44). The blank shape must remain intact while the 'corner' is cut away on the back face from the trailing edge to a point about $\frac{1}{16}$ in. down in the front face from the top. On a propeller for rubber drive, there should be a concave undercamber in the blade, and both sides must

130

be completely sanded smooth to final under profile *before* work is started on the top.

Mark a high camber point on the top of the blank, about 25 per cent of the blade width back from the leading edge and cut away from the trailing edge forward to this marked line. The forward 25 per cent is then rubbed down to form a curved leading edge, blending into a radius at the front to round out with the underside.

Most important is the angle of the hole through which the shaft runs. This *must* be square from all views. If it is drilled at the blank stage then its accuracy is more certain.

Remember always to check that you are not carving for wrong rotation, or that you have each blade set for opposite rotation! These sound like foolish errors but are in fact commonplace, especially among novices. Anti-clockwise rotation is normal, as the majority of model engines are designed and port timed for that rotation, and the pusher propeller must therefore have blades which are 'twisted' to bite the air when viewed *anti*-clockwise from the front. It is this which causes much confusion, and results in peculiar blade angles for those who do not stop to consider which way to carve a pusher prop.

MOULDING COCKPIT COVERS

There are two basic methods of moulding a cockpit cover, the *stretch* and *pressure* approaches, and they are used according to the shape required. If the cabin is a large moulding with not very involved shapes, the stretch method is best. Otherwise a small 'bubble' canopy or intricately curved windshield needs to be made by the pressure method.

Each system uses acetate sheet. This is a clear cellulose acetate plastic, sold at model shops and art stores. Get ·02 in. thickness if possible. The thicker, the stronger the mould.

Shape the cabin or canopy in wood. It can be balsa, which is then filled and polished, for all the irregularities will show in the moulding. In the same way one can apply irregularities in the form of card strips to get an impression of canopy structure or indentations that exist in the real aircraft canopy (Fig. 45).

For the stretch method, the wooden dummy canopy must be firmly mounted on an extension in a vice. Take a sheet of acetate of ample size and pin the ends of the rectangle to stout sticks. Use plenty of

131

steel pins at about 2-in. intervals, about ¾ in. from the outer edges. Now hold the sheet in front of an electric fire with about 18 in. air gap. This heats the acetate which will steam and give off a vapour. It

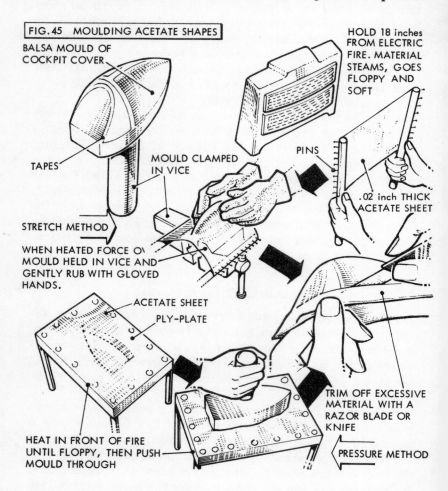

FIG. 45 MOULDING ACETATE SHAPES

BALSA MOULD OF COCKPIT COVER

HOLD 18 inches FROM ELECTRIC FIRE. MATERIAL STEAMS, GOES FLOPPY AND SOFT

TAPES

MOULD CLAMPED IN VICE

PINS

.02 inch THICK ACETATE SHEET

STRETCH METHOD

WHEN HEATED FORCE OV MOULD HELD IN VICE AND GENTLY RUB WITH GLOVED HANDS.

ACETATE SHEET

PLY-PLATE

TRIM OFF EXCESSIVE MATERIAL WITH A RAZOR BLADE OR KNIFE

HEAT IN FRONT OF FIRE UNTIL FLOPPY, THEN PUSH MOULD THROUGH

PRESSURE METHOD

will soften and go floppy but must not be taken too near the fire or it will overheat and bubbles appear inside the acetate structure. Steady warming, lasting up to 5 min., will get the acetate to a floppy state where it is easily dented by a gloved finger.

Now have an assistant ready, also glove protected from the hot acetate. In one swift move, plunge the acetate over the wood dummy and have the assistant rub and push the acetate on to the wood surface while you pull and stretch with the stout sticks. The acetate cools quickly, holding shape, and can be trimmed to actual size with a knife or razor-blade.

The pressure method calls for the same type of wooden dummy plus a ply plate with about 3 in. surrounding clearance around the profile of the dummy. A hole is cut in the ply with $\frac{3}{32}$ in. clearance all around the dummy profile so that it can pass through with the acetate attached. Now pin a rectangle of acetate over the ply at about 2-in. intervals, all around the edge. Heat the acetate as for the stretch method then push the ply over the wooden form so that it pressure forces the acetate to adopt the curves as it projects through the hole. This method produces bubble canopies up to 12 in. long and 3 in. deep. Sometimes the first attempt does not produce sufficient stretch in the material but re-heating and even several attempts will get the final result. Any milkiness or 'blushing' can be removed by wiping over the spot with a quick coat of cellulose thinners. Bubbles cannot be removed.

AUTO-RUDDERS

Most model gliders have this device as an aid to towing for the launch. The model has a small rudder which sets the rate of turn, but when the glider is being towed on the end of a line for the launch at height, the rudder would have a serious turning effect. In consequence it is neutralized by the engagement of the towline on the tow hook. A curtain ring is the ubiquitous choice for the end of the towline, and as this slips over the towhook it either directly pulls a line or swings a bar so that a line from the rudder is pulled to straighten the rudder. As the ring is freed on release, so the rudder is returned for flight setting by tension of a rubber band.

Similar auto-rudders are engaged with engine timers on power models to produce a glide turn with an angle of rudder setting that would court danger if exposed to a fast propeller slipstream. Thus the rudder is neutral for the climb, and is so timed to come on to glide setting a split second before the engine stops. This will throw the model into a tight turn as the last power moments die off, and the model does not lose height in a stall. Transition from power to glide in such a turn is all-important for contest models.

REFINEMENTS, HINTS AND TIPS

The experts have two clockwork timers in a power model, and they are extensively modified to obtain positive action with 100 per cent efficiency, otherwise their value is questionable. The timer which actuates the auto-rudder and the power shut-off valve is set for 10 sec. duration in the majority of cases. All the international and many domestic contests are for power runs of 10 sec. The other timer will run for 3 min. and then trips a 'dethermalizer'. It can also be used for other functions.

DETHERMALIZERS

Unstable air conditions are prevalent. Differences of ground temperature over grass, runways, buildings, corn, etc., create thermal breakaways with fast upcurrents of hot air surrounded by descending cool air to fill-in and become 'downdraughts'. A model with wing loading of up to 10 oz. per sq. ft. will be taken up at 6 ft. per sec. on average in a British thermal, and would come down almost as fast in a downdraught. The object is naturally enough to catch the thermal but more often than not the flyer releases his model into the area of 'down'. Such is fortune!

Contests have maximum times of 3 min. duration, as we have already explained. Thus, there is little point in having a model fly for more than 3 min. and we employ a dethermalizer to destroy lift and bring the model down safely in near vertical descent.

First dethermalizers were pop-up extra fins, intended to 'weather-cock' the model and head it clear of the thermal and into the surrounding downdraught. Although admirable in concept, the idea was a failure as invariably the thermal still held the model, and quite often when the grip on the model was lost, a straight flight down-wind only took the model farther away from base.

Then the parachute came into vogue. Made of tissue or silk and deployed from the tail or halfway along the fuselage, the trailing parachute effectively brought the model down in most cases except in very strong thermals, but resulted in many broken models as the descent was usually a dive. The drag parachute is ideal as a temporary arrangement as it can be wrapped and stowed along the fuselage side prior to release. It also is structurally safer than the tipping tail for very large models (gliders) of 10 ft. span or more (Fig. 46).

The tipping tail is quite definitely the better system for most models. Action is simple in that the whole tailplane tilts upwards (trailing

134

edge high, or leading edge low according to above or below fuselage position of the tailplane) at 35–40 deg. All lift is destroyed and the model descends nearly vertically like a parachute. If the tail tip is too great the descent will be fast. If it is not enough, the result will be a succession of whipstalls on the descent.

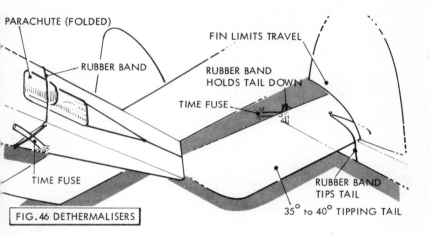

FIG. 46 DETHERMALISERS

The tail is released from its normal flight position by either the destruction of a retaining rubber band which is burned through by a lampwick fuse, or by release of a mechanical trip through a clock-work timer. Sometimes, working on 'belt and braces' principles, both systems are employed. The fuse comes with a red thread in it, and standard burning time is 90 sec. between marks, so that the fuse can be set reasonably accurately for 3 min. with a double mark gap at the launch. Fuse can be set alight by match or cigarette, at both ends for safety, and then adjusted by pulling through the band it is intended to burn.

The mechanical trip arrangement is an equally simple connection of a wire to a bellcrank which is held down while the timer is running to the 3-min. stage. Then the timer allows the wire to move the bell-crank which allows a rubber band to slip off and set the tail up. Whole action is accelerated by rubber bands over the leading edge of the tailplane and these will pull the tail forward and up against a stop to limit the angle.

REFINEMENTS, HINTS AND TIPS

FOLDING PROPELLERS

When the power run of a rubber-driven model is exhausted, there is a danger that the windmilling airscrew, still connected to the motor, and liable to stop at an awkward position, could upset trim and bring the model down in a spiral dive. This is inevitable if a propeller sticks in set position. On a power model, the blade area is not sufficient to create any trouble, but with the large blades on rubber types, the angles of pitch and drag are such that the blades must do one of three things. They must go into a neutral angle or 'feather', they can free-wheel, or they can fold in the airstream.

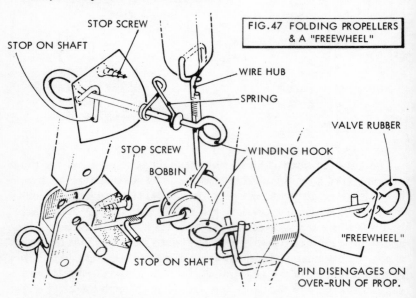

FIG. 47 FOLDING PROPELLERS & A "FREEWHEEL"

STOP SCREW

STOP ON SHAFT

WIRE HUB

SPRING

STOP SCREW

BOBBIN

WINDING HOOK

VALVE RUBBER

"FREEWHEEL"

STOP ON SHAFT

PIN DISENGAGES ON OVER-RUN OF PROP.

By far the most popular method in modern aeromodelling is the folding blade. It streamlines the airframe, is simple and allows the blades to be made independently from sheet balsa instead of from one large block. Only snags are that the hub, with hinges, must be strong and accurately made. There are many approaches, using wire and wooden hubs, the former being more common. Some systems incorporate blade angle change adjustment. All have a stop on the shaft so that the blades will come to rest alongside the fuselage in the same position each flight. This is in the form of a screw set into the

136

rear face of the nose block and arranged to engage an extension on the rotating shaft when the rubber motor tension is reduced to a certain point. A spring tensioner between the propeller hub and the noseblock pulls the shaft forward relative to its bearing in the noseblock, as the power runs out. Rotation stops as the screw head catches the shaft and the sudden action plus slipstream sends the blades backwards into folded position (Fig. 47).

FREE-WHEELING PROPELLERS

By allowing the prop to windmill as the model descends in a glide, drag is reduced and there is no danger of a trim upset. It simply means that the propeller is engaged with a clutch on the shaft, and when rubber power runs out, then the prop disengages automatically and runs free. There are many types of clutch; but they all have a common base in a loop of wire on the shaft through which the clutch pin fits. A loop is also formed at the front end of the shaft to engage with an appropriate winding hook, fitted to a hand drill.

MAKING UP FUELS

Where bulk supply of the basic constituents in model aero engine fuels is to hand, one can effect a great economy by mixing one's own fuel. Cost of can, spout, and label are saved at least; but it must be emphasized that many fuel blenders have their own pet additives and oils which offer better performance.

For general flying, the 'home-brew' mixture is usually adequate. *Glowplug* engines have Methyl Alcohol (Methanol) as the main base and an elementary mix is 70 per cent Methanol 30 per cent castor oil. One can get Methanol through motorcycle garages which cater for the sportsman, and Castrol M.S.S.R. is a good synthetic oil widely used to replace Castor. Two additives which are not only expensive but hard to get, are Nitro benzine and Nitro methane. Up to 10 per cent of the former and 50 per cent of the latter, replacing part of the Methanol, will give an increase of power. Even only 5 per cent Nitro methane has an effect in making an engine more flexible to tune on the needle valve. Sometimes it is necessary to add a few drops of Acetone as a solvent to get the Nitro and Castor to mix properly. Always keep Methanol stoppered as it will absorb moisture, and shield Nitro methane from strong light.

137

REFINEMENTS, HINTS AND TIPS

Diesel engines use ether, paraffin and castor oil as basics. Equal parts of each will provide a general workable fuel, but it is better to ration the percentages to 30 ether, 50 paraffin and 20 castor oil. At high speeds, these formulae need a few drops per pint of Amyl Nitrate or Amyl Nitrite to act as an ignition lag and so stop misfire. More than 3 per cent is a waste, so the 'dope' can be bought in small quantities through a dispensing chemist. The ether need not be best grade. 'Ether Meths', S.G. 720 is free of water and ideal for a model fuel. Always store away from fire risks.

CHAPTER 13

———————— ◎ ————————

Repairs

———————— ◎ ————————

Accidents *will* happen! An ungracious gust of wind at the wrong time, a sloppy wing fit, a broken rubber motor or a loose engine will send the model bowling tail over tip, breaking parts in the process. Wrecks always look bad to the owner. His pride and joy take a hard tumble and when wings snap in the middle, or a couple of longerons break, the modeller often takes the view that he'll salvage the hardware and burn the rest to make a fresh start on a new model.

You will never find the 'old school' of aeromodellers scrapping the pieces, nor will the ingenious type ever discard what might at first sight be irreparable.

First thoughts *must* always be *not* what is the damage; but *what caused the crash?* Otherwise there might be a repeat action next time out. Try to reason out all the probabilities and narrow them down to a few essential modifications. At the same time, protect open breaks in wood from any fuel soakage which will make a joint hard to stick, and then stow the heap away overnight and forget it, if possible! This is an infallible cure for gloom and despondency that has worked for many years. The serious crash, which cannot be tackled on the field, always looks less formidable after the modeller has enjoyed a good night of sleep!

JIGGING

There is only one way to make sure that the model will be repaired to its original state, and that is by jigging each component. This means making a set of braces to hold the remaining parts of the structure at the correct angles relative to one another. For example, a wing may lose a few ribs and a spar section. Here, the replacement

139

ribs must be cut ready to insert while the leading and trailing edges are firmly braced by pinning to a building board. New spar sections need not be in the same position as before, in fact it is an advantage to stagger the new spar by its own thickness so that it overlaps what remained intact and the overlap becomes the joint as spars meet face to face. Always try to refit whole new ribs, a patched rib is heavier than it needs to be, and repairs in wings are apt to make one panel heavier than its opposite, with an effect on the flight trim (Fig. 48).

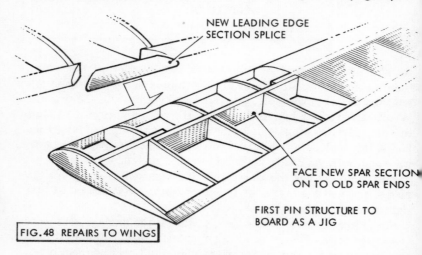

NEW LEADING EDGE
SECTION SPLICE

FACE NEW SPAR SECTION
ON TO OLD SPAR ENDS

FIRST PIN STRUCTURE TO
BOARD AS A JIG

FIG. 48 REPAIRS TO WINGS

If a couple of longerons have broken, the fuselage cannot be pinned to the building board, so here it is even more essential to have accurate jigging. The critical factors will be the angles of the thrust-line, the wing and tailplane incidences, and the overall balance which must all be retained. Check the plan for the decalage (difference in wing and tail angles) and make up a jig from card or sheet balsa to ensure that the fuselage side profile is braced to keep the wing and tail correctly sited (Fig. 49).

Splice in sections of new longerons; but in addition, fit gussets to the spliced area so that the accident will be resisted on another fateful occasion. If a sheet balsa insert, filling the damaged area, is thought to be a better proposition, consider the question of overall balance first. Repairs to the tail end of a model, however light in grammes they may seem to be, need ounces to balance up at the nose. This is particularly the case in gliders.

REPAIRS

Before setting oneself the target of completely making good any large repair, one ought to reason out, with logic, the pros and cons of the situation. It could be that damage to a nose section indicates that the same thing will happen repeatedly in the future. This would be a clear-cut recommendation for a glass fibre overlay to protect and strengthen the outer skin. If the break was in the tail end, the most one could do would be to strengthen the joint with balsa.

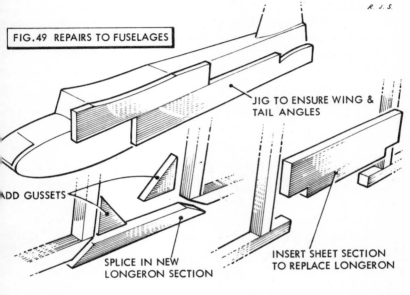

R. J. S.

FIG.49 REPAIRS TO FUSELAGES

JIG TO ENSURE WING & TAIL ANGLES

ADD GUSSETS

SPLICE IN NEW LONGERON SECTION

INSERT SHEET SECTION TO REPLACE LONGERON

There is also a problem in the case of repairing parts which have been coated with protective fuel proofer, or the surface has been varnished. Only solution is to cut the coating from the surrounding area, for there should be no concession to the strength of the glue joint. Attaching covering and matching in colours on a protected surface also calls for etching back the surrounds so that the patch of new covering can key in securely. What will seem to be drastic action is usually the best line of approach. There is nothing more obvious than a 'botched' job. A larger scale repair is usually quicker too. While one has been fussing about with small patches and sections of rib, etc., a section of a new wing panel could perhaps have been made.

141

DENTED SHEETING

This is a common break, applicable to leading edge covering on wings on fuselage sides. Cut the opposite side of the wing so that access can be gained to the rear surface of the sheet balsa and then insert a patch in sheet wood of similar thickness so that there will be a two-ply of crossed grain. Fit a wedge to push the patch and fill out the dent on the outer surface. On a fuselage there is often access through a cabin roof. If there is no access, cut away the dented area using an angle cut and making the cuts over adjacent ribs or spacers. The appearance of the edges of the hole now made should resemble a picture frame with mitred corners (Fig. 50). Use the piece cut away

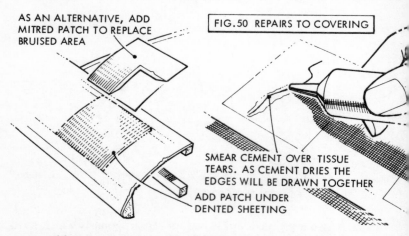

AS AN ALTERNATIVE, ADD MITRED PATCH TO REPLACE BRUISED AREA

FIG. 50 REPAIRS TO COVERING

SMEAR CEMENT OVER TISSUE TEARS. AS CEMENT DRIES THE EDGES WILL BE DRAWN TOGETHER

ADD PATCH UNDER DENTED SHEETING

as a guide to cut a new patch, Set 'shelves' in place, made of something like $\frac{1}{16}$ in. $\times \frac{1}{4}$ in. balsa, glued for half of the $\frac{1}{4}$-in. width to the underside of any unsupported surrounding sheet. Use a slow-drying glue and position the patch, holding in place with Scotch tape, Sellotape, or, if not disturbed by pinning, use modelling pins.

RE-COVERING

After several coats of dope, clear and coloured, have been applied to a model, it becomes specially difficult to remove all the tissue or fabric from the surface for a fresh re-covering. This is specially annoying if one wishes to apply a different colour of tissue on a

REPAIRS

lightweight model, where the tissue dye remains permanent on the wood. Sandpaper is the only cure that really works. One can try rubbing with a thinners-soaked rag, or scraping with a sharp razor-blade; but experience is that only an abrasive with even action will satisfactorily remove existing covering.

Making a patch re-covering over a section of fuselage side is not difficult but the simple precaution of making sure that the tissue or fabric 'grain' is in the same direction as before will obviate a 'tell-tale' patch.

When patching rib bays, there is a risk of losing the tautness of covering in adjacent bays. In consequence, do *not* cut away the torn tissue unless necessary, until the new patch is ready for application. Then the tension in the tissue will only have a short period in which to relax. Always use dope as an adhesive and work the patch well with the forefingers so that it is stretched as tightly as possible across the repaired area. Sometimes it is definitely beneficial to stick just one side of the patch in place, then to allow this to dry securely so that the patch can be pulled and the existing covering also tensioned by the same action before the opposite edge(s) are stuck down.

Tissue Tears

Most prevalent form of damage is the tissue tear caused by thistles, corn stalks, tree landings or mishandling. If it is a straight slit, then a thin smear of balsa cement will bring the edges together very quickly and almost completely disguise the blemish. Cement shrinks quickly and even irregular tears can be brought together by tackling the repair with a series of 'spot welds' to pull tears in-line first, before smearing over the cracks. If the tissue has been pushed in and does not appear to want to pop back in place, try sucking at the area with the open mouth. This usually draws out the offending tissue. Fabrics can be treated in the same way; but of course are less prone to tear in the first instance.

Field Repairs

Faster drying cements than those normally used for construction, can be obtained for field use, but there may not even be time allowance in a competition to get a full repair executed. One has to resort to ingenuity, and here, the faithful standby reels of Scotch tape and

Sellotape are invaluable. A hole can be covered, a wing lashed in place, bracing 'struts' made or even halves of fuselages held together for the all-important last flight of the day. The field repair kit should contain pins, razor-blades, thread, spare bolts and nuts, tissue, balsa, a spare engine needle valve, ballast weight, wire, and the tapes. Try to be a good Scout and '*Be Prepared*', for as long as the modeller has the materials handy, the accident rarely happens!

Bibliography

AEROMODELLING MAGAZINES

(including those with occasional Aeromodelling features)

Aeromodeller: 13/35 Bridge Street, Hemel Hempstead, Herts., England.
Aero Modelar: 12 Dalmatinska, Zagreb, Yugoslavia.
Aero Revue: Lidostrasse 5, 6006 Lucerne 15, Switzerland.
Airfix Magazine: Bar Hill, Cambridge, CB3 8EL.
American Modeler: 733 Fifteenth Street, N.W., Washington, DC. 20005.
Flug Modell-Technik: Hardstrasse 3, Baden-Baden, West Germany.
Flying Models: Box 65 Centereach, L.I., N.Y., U.S.A.
Ilmailu: Mannerheiminitie 16A, Helsinki, Finland.
Letecky Modelar: Lublanska 57, Praha 2, Czechoslovakia.
Modelarz: ul Chocimska 14, Warsaw, Poland.
Modellistica: Borgo Pinti 99r., Firenze, Italy.
Le Modèle Réduit D'Avion: 74 Rue Bonaparte, Paris 6e, France.
Modellbau und Basteln: Langenbeckstrasse 36–39 Neuenhagen b., East Berlin, East Germany.
Modellezes: Engels ter. 14, Budapest V, Hungary.
Model Airplane News: White Plains Plaza, 1 No. Broadway, White Plains, N.Y. 10601, U.S.A.
Model Builder: 1900 E. Edinger Ave., Santa Ana, California, U.S.A., 92705.
Radio Control Models and Electronics: 13/35 Bridge Street, Hemel Hempstead, Herts., England.
Radio Modeller: 64 Wellington Road, Hampton Hill, Middlesex.
Radio Control Technique: 3 Jinbocho Kanda, Chiyoda-ku, Tokyo, Japan.
Radio Control Modeler: Box 487, Sierra Madre, Calif. 91024, U.S.A.

K   145

Aeromodelling Specifications

INTERNATIONAL MODEL SPECIFICATIONS

General

Size: Not more than 2,325 sq. in. projected area.

Weight: Not more than 11·023 lb. except multi-engined scale Control-line (15·452 lb.).

Loading:
Free Flight:	between 3·95 oz./sq. ft. and 16.38 oz./sq. ft.
Control Line:	between 3·95 oz./sq. ft. and 32·76 oz./sq. ft.
Scale C/L:	between 3·95 oz./sq. ft. and 49·12 oz./sq. ft.
Radio Control:	between 3·95 oz./sq. ft. and 24·51 oz./sq. ft.
Scale R/C:	between 3·95 oz./sq. ft. and 32·76 oz./sq. ft.

Power: Internal combustion engine(s) used must not exceed 10 cc. Multi-engined Control Line scale models may total up to 20 cc. Jets should not weigh more than 2·2 lb. or less than 1·1 lb.

Launching: By hand or rise off ground according to contest. Gliders by means of an extensible tow-line 164 ft. long, carrying a 39 sq. in. pennant.

Identification: All models carry the competitor's licence or membership number with the National registration letters/numbers.

Types: (Free Flight)

A/2 GLIDER

Size: 496–527 sq. in. total projected area.

Weight: 14·46 oz. minimum.

WAKEFIELD

Size: 263·5 to 294·5 sq. in. total projected area.

Weight: 8·11 oz. minimum with motor.

Power: 40 gm. rubber, lubricated weight (maximum).

F.A.I. POWER

Size: Unrestricted except by area loading regulations.

Weight: 10·58 oz. per cc. minimum.

Loading: 6·55 oz./sq. ft. to 16·38 oz./sq. ft.

Power: 2·5 cc. maximum engine capacity, 10 seconds max. run from release.

Flights for above are of 3 minutes maximum duration in 7 rounds.

INDOOR

Size: Unrestricted except by 25$\frac{9}{16}$ in. max. wingspan.

Weight:
Loading: } Unrestricted.

AEROMODELLING SPECIFICATIONS

Power: Rubber drive only.

Flights: 6 launches, better 2 count.

N.B. For record purposes this category is divided by ceiling heights: Cat. I up to 26 ft., Cat. II up to 49 ft., Cat. III up to 98 ft., Cat. IV over 98 ft.

Types: (Control-Line)

AEROBATICS

Size:

Weight: } Power, etc. as above, under Generai.

Loading:

Line length: Between 49·2 ft. and 70·5 ft.

Pull test: 15 × weight of model up to 40·4 lb. maximum.

SPEED

Size:

Weight: } As under General.

Loading:

Area: 31 sq. in. per cc. engine capacity.

Power: 2·5 cc. maximum.

Fuel: 80/20 or 75/25 methanol/castor oil or any 'diesel' formula for compression ignition.

Line length: 15·92 m. (52 ft. 2¾ in.) 2 × 0·30mm.

Pull test: 20 × weight of model.

TEAM RACE

Size: 186 sq. in. minimum total projected area.

Weight: 24·69 oz. maximum.

Fuselage: 4 × 2 in. at cockpit (min. cross-section area 6.045 sq. in.).

Tank: 7 cc. maximum capacity.

Wheels: 1 in. minimum dia.

Power: 2·5 cc. maximum engine capacity.

Line length: 52 ft. 2¾ in. (2 × 0·30mm)

Pull test: 20 × weight of model.

COMBAT

Size: Unrestricted except by area loading regulations.

Power: 2·5 cc. maximum engine capacity.

Line length: 52 ft. 2¾ in.

SOCIETY OF MODEL AERONAUTICAL ENGINEERS MODEL SPECIFICATIONS

Types: (Free Flight)

UNRESTRICTED CLASSES*

Glider: (Only general restrictions apply concerning maximum area and weight.)

Power: (Only general restrictions apply concerning maximum area, weight and engine capacity.)

Rubber: (Only general restrictions apply concerning maximum area and weight.)

* Flights in this class are of 3 minutes maximum in 3 rounds.

AEROMODELLING SPECIFICATIONS

Types: (Control-Line)

A TEAM RACE

Size: 90 sq. in. min. total projected area.
Fuselage: 3 in. × 1·5 in. at cockpit.
Tank: 6 cc. max. capacity.
Wheels: 1 in. dia. – ⅛ in. for wear.
Power: 1.5 cc. max. engine capacity.
Line length: 46 ft. 8 in. (2 × ·010 in. dia.).

A TEAM RACE

     All specifications identical to International Class.

B TEAM RACE

Size: 133 sq. in. min. total projected area.
Fuselage: 4 in. × 2 in. min. total projected area.
Tank: 30 cc. max. capacity.
Wheels: 1 in. dia. – ⅛ in. for wear.
Power: 2·51–5 cc. engines.
Pull test: 20 × weight of model.
Line length: 60 ft. (2 × 0·0124 in. dia.).

A COMBAT

     All specifications identical to International Class.

B COMBAT

Size: Unrestricted except by area loading regulations.
Power: 2·51–6·55 cc. capacity.
Line length: 60 ft. ± 3 in.
Pull test: None.

SPEED

CLASS 1:
Power: 1·5 cc.
Line length: 47 ft. 5¾ in. (No set dia.)

CLASS 2:
Power: 1·51 cc.–2·5 cc.
Line length: 52 ft. 2¾ in. (No set dia.)

CLASS 3:

     All specifications as International Class.

CLASS 4:
Power: 2·51 cc.–5 cc.
Line length: 58 ft. ½ in. (No set dia.)

CLASS 5:
Power: 5·01 cc.–10 cc.
Line length: 63 ft. 3¼ in. (No set dia.)
Fuel: Unrestricted except the use of Tetra-nitromethane or Dioxan is banned.
Pull test: Thirty times model weight sustained for 10 seconds for speed models.

Recommended minimum diameters of control lines for speed models:

CLASS 1:   Monoline ·0108 (32 s.w.g.)—Two lines ·0076 (36 s.w.g.).
CLASS 2:   Monoline ·0137 (29 s.w.g.)—Two lines ·010 (33 s.w.g.).
CLASS 4:   Monoline ·0148 (28 s.w.g.)—Two lines ·0108 (32 s.w.g.).
CLASS 5:   Monoline ·020 (25 s.w.g.)—Two lines ·0148 (28 s.w.g.).

AEROMODELLING SPECIFICATIONS

AEROBATICS
All specifications identical to International Class.

RAT RACE
Size: Unrestricted except by area loading regulations.
Power: 6·55 cc. maximum.
Line length: 60 ft. 2 × 0·0148 in. dia. (28 s.w.g.).
Pull test: None but safety inspection.

Special Classes

PAYLOAD*
Size: Unrestricted.
Power: Up to 0·82 cc. for 5 oz. ballast, up to 1 cc. for 6 oz. ballast.
Ballast: 4 oz. in dummy pilot to special specification plus cargo of 1 or 2 oz.

   N.B. All flights must rise off ground.

TAILLESS*
Size: Unrestricted.
Power: Glider, Rubber or up to 10 cc. (Engine run 15 seconds.)

  * Flights in these classes are of 3 minutes maximum in 3 rounds.

ROUND-THE-POLE
Size: Unrestricted except that speed models shall have wing span at least 60 per cent of length and not weigh more than 8 oz.
Pole height: Class A—36 in.   Class B—72 in.   Speed 18 in.
Line length: Class A—72 in.   Class B—144 in.   Speed 66 in.

Glossary

Technical terms and abbreviations used in Aeromodelling

A/1: Glider classification, lifting surface area not exceeding 279 sq. ins. Nordic origin, adopted by many nations for competitions.

A/2: Glider classification, lifting surface area 496–527 sq. ins. Nordic origin, adopted internationally for World Championships.

ACTUATOR: Mechanical device to operate model component, usually radio controlled and driven by rubber motor or clockwork.

AERIAL: Receiving antenna on radio control equipment or transmission antenna on transmitter.

AEROBATICS: Manœuvres performed by an aeroplane.

AEROFOIL: Cross section of a lifting surface also known as AIRFOIL or RIB SECTION.

AIR INTAKE: Induction tube on a model engine through which fuel is syphoned from the tank.

AIRSCREW: Means of converting power to thrust by engine shaft, also known as PROPELLER.

ANGLE OF ATTACK: The angle at which the lifting surfaces are presented to the air in flight.

ANGLE OF INCIDENCE: Angle of lifting surfaces relative to the datum line of the model.

ANHEDRAL: Angle at which tips of lifting surfaces are depressed downwards from the horizontal.

ASPECT RATIO: Ratio of width to span.

AUTOGYRO: Rotating wing aircraft with conventional propeller thrust and air driven rotor.

AUTO-RUDDER: Device to change direction of flight automatically at particular flight stage.

BALSA: Spanish for 'raft'. Timber originating in Ecuador of very light grade used extensively for aeromodelling.

BAMBOO: Cane, split for use in modelling.

BANANA OIL: Non-shrinking clear cellulose.

BANK: Lateral angle adopted by an aeroplane in a turn.

BASS: Close-grained soft wood suitable for carved scale models.

BEARER: Hardwood rail to support engine or internal equipment in a model.

BEARING: Tubular fitting, for example wheel axle, propeller shaft support.

BEECH: Recommended hard wood for engine bearers.

BELLCRANK: Angled lever for transmission of push-pull action at 90 deg.

BIPLANE: Aeroplane with two mainplanes usually arranged one above the other.

BRACE: Extra support for holding wing spar angles, etc.

BULKHEAD: Solid vertical cross sectional fuselage component to maintain shape.

BUSH: Bearing, tubular in section, as used for rotary shafts.

CAM: Eccentric shape mounted on a shaft.

CAMBER: Curvature of the wing surface in cross section.

CAP STRIP: Flat strip over ribs in wing or tail for covering support.

CARBURETTOR: Means of fuel induction, providing atomization of fuel and air.

CEMENT: Quick-drying adhesive.

CENTRE SECTION: Area of wing adjacent to fuselage, or centre, flat portion of wing.

CENTRE OF PRESSURE: Point on upper surface of the wing at which lift can be said to centre.

C.G. (Centre of gravity): Point at which the model will balance in both horizontal and vertical planes.

CHOKE: To completely cover a carburettor intake.

CHORD: Lifting surface width.

C.L.: Centre line.

COIL: Wire winding, used as a radio control component. Also means of inducing high voltage spark for ignition.

COMBAT: Where two models fly simultaneously endeavouring to cut towed streamers trailing from the rear of each model.

COMPRESSION IGNITION: Spontaneous combustion caused by compression of volatile fuel.

CONDENSER: Smoothing device for electrical circuit in spark ignition or radio control.

CONTROL-LINE: Means of controlling model flight by tethering line(s).

COWLING: Enclosing panel around engine compartment, detachable for inspection.

CRANKSHAFT: Revolving shaft driven by piston to convert internal combustion power to torque, enclosed in crankcase.

CUBIC CAPACITY: Volume of cylinder displaced by piston (stroke × area of bore).

GLOSSARY

DATUM: Construction line about which all angles are relative.

DECALAGE: Angular difference between lifting surfaces of wing and elevator.

DELTA: Triangular platform flying wing.

DETHERMALIZER: Device to destroy lift efficiency and bring model out of thermal.

DIESEL: Common term for compression ignition engine.

DIHEDRAL: Upward and outward sweep of lifting surface.

DOPE: Nitrate, butyrate or cellulose finishing liquid, quick drying.

DOWEL: Circular cross section wooden rod.

DOWNTHRUST: Forward and downward angle of thrust line relative to datum.

DRAG: Resistance of movement through surface friction in air.

DUMMY: Non-working scale replica of a component.

DURATION: Expired time from moment of release to when model is lost from view or flight terminates.

ELECTRODE: Wire points in a sparking plug across which spark jumps.

ELEVATOR: Movable control surface to raise or lower angle of attack.

EMPENNAGE: Complete tail unit with horizontal and vertical surfaces.

ESCAPEMENT: Mechanical ratchet arranged to move a control surface or operate a component according to selective signal.

F.A.I. (Fédération Aéronautique Internationale): Governing body for all forms of aviation and international committee for establishment of rules and records.

FALSE ATTEMPT: Discounted flight of less than 20 sec. or caused by collision or similar misfortune.

FALSE RIB: Short wing rib used to maintain airfoil section at leading edge.

FILLER: Means of sealing wood grain or tissue pores.

FIN: Fixed portion of vertical tail.

FIREWALL: Bulkhead immediately behind engine.

FLAP: Movable surface of wing used to increase camber for lift.

FLOAT: Supporting waterproof form for models operating from water.

FLYING BOAT: Model capable of rising off water using a boat-type hull plus sponsons or outrigger floats near tips.

FLYING SCALE: Replica of full-size man-carrying machine, scaled in all dimensions.

FLYING WING: Model without tail surfaces.

FORMER: Shaped vertical cross section member of fuselage not necessarily of solid structure as bulkhead.

GLOSSARY

Free Flight: Auto-stable models not requiring control during flight.

Freewheel: Disengaging clutch permitting airscrew to windmill.

Fuselage: Body of an aircraft supporting wings and tail surfaces.

Geodetic: Basket weave type construction with diagonal spars.

Glider: Model designed to fly with gravity as motive thrust.

G-Line: Form of control line with single line elevated or depressed by fishing rod.

Glowplug: Ignition plug with platinum wire coil rendered incandescent by short circuit, maintaining subsequent compression ignition.

Hand Launch: Release of a model in forward motion from the hand.

Hand Winder: Geared drill adapted to apply turns on rubber motor.

Helicopter: Aeroplane supported by power-driven rotor(s).

Horn: Lever attached to control surface.

Hovercraft: Air-riding machine supported by impelled air out of base.

Hydro Model: Model capable of landing and taking-off water.

Ignition: Means of exploding combustible fuel.

Incidence: Angle of lifting surface relative to datum.

Induced Drag: Resistance of an airframe to forward movement through disturbance of atmosphere.

Instability: Aerodynamic state whereby model does not recover normal flying attitude after disturbance.

Jap Tissue: Lightweight covering paper, hand-made in Japan.

Jet: Propulsive unit providing thrust through jet reaction.

Jetex: Commercial solid fuel rocket device.

Jig: Fixture for relating component parts.

Keel: Profile or backbone used to obtain true fuselage shape.

Kit: Pack of components for making a specific model.

Kite: Colloquial term for model. Otherwise tethered shape with tail stabilizer.

Laminate: Several layers of material joined on surfaces to give added strength.

Landing Gear: Also undercarriage, supports model while at rest and during take-off and landing.

Lateral Stability: Ability to recover to normal flight condition after disturbance from the side, about the horizontal axis of the fuselage.

Leading Edge: The front edge of a lifting surface.

Lift: Vertical component which supports the model in flight, overcoming gravity.

GLOSSARY

LONGERON: Principal structure in a fuselage, longitudinal spars.

LOOP: Aerobatic manœuvre where model describes a circle about a horizontal axis.

LUBRICANT: Glycerine-based solution used on rubber motors to prevent chafing or oil content in two-stroke engine fuel formula.

MAINPLANE: Principal lifting surface or wing.

MICROFILM: Very light film covering for indoor models.

MOMENT ARM: The distance between the centre of pressures of wing and tail surfaces or wing and thrust point, forming a lever of action.

MONOLINE: Means of control-line flying through application of torsion on the line.

MOTOR BEARER: Hardwood rail supporting engine.

MOTOR RUN: Duration of applied power.

MOTOR STICK: Rigid strip of wood used to form a fuselage on stick-type model with exposed engine or rubber motor.

NACELLE: Fairing supporting a wing-mounted engine.

NATIONALS: Annual championships meetings organized by governing bodies in most countries where modelling is regulated by an organization.

NEGATIVE ANGLE: Depressed angle of incidence on tailplane or depressed thrust line.

NOSEBLOCK: Shaped block used to support the propeller shaft bearing.

O.O.S.: Out of sight.

ORNITHOPTER: Model simulating birdlike flight by flapping wings.

PARACHUTE: Airbrake used to dethermalize a model or retard deposited accessories.

PARASOL: Mounting supporting a wing above a fuselage by struts.

PAXOLIN: Fibrous material used for bearings and radio chassis.

PAYLOAD: Disposable load fitted to special type models.

PITCH: Distance travelled by a propeller tip in one revolution.

PLANFORM: Outline of a model viewed from above.

PLANKING: Wood covering by means of narrow tapered strips.

PLYWOOD: Laminated veneers crossgrained for rigidity.

POD: Short-nose section of fuselage where a thinner tailboom exists.

POLYHEDRAL: Application of more than two dihedral breaks on a lifting surface.

POSITIVE INCIDENCE: Upward angle of wing relative to datum.

PROPELLER: Propulsive airscrew usually of pusher type unless termed a tractor propeller.

GLOSSARY

PROTOTYPE: First design of a series.

PTERODACTYL: Tailless aeroplane with swept wings.

PULLEY LAUNCH: Single-handed tow launch with the aid of a fixed pulley or pulleys.

PUSHER: An aeroplane with propeller at the rear and motor forward of it.

PYLON: Vertical support for a wing surface.

RADIO CONTROL (R/C): Means of remote control by transmission of radio signal.

RATIO: Relative comparison between factors, as for example, between power run and glide duration.

RECEIVER: Electrical circuit located in a model for reception of radio signals.

REED: Vibrating metal strip used to distinguish audio tones from a receiver.

REED VALVE: Induction valve used for pulse jets and some model engines.

RELAY: Electrical solenoid for switching servo or actuator on radio signal.

RETRACTING UNDERCARRIAGE: Landing gear which will retire into airframe for streamlining.

RIB: Surface component used to maintain aerofoil cross section.

RISER: A thermal or rising warm current of air.

R.O.G.: Rise off ground.

ROOT: End rib on lifting surface adjacent to fuselage or centre section.

R.O.W.: Rise off water.

RUDDER: Movable portion of vertical tail surface.

SAILPLANE: Model capable of soaring flight without motive power.

SCALE MODEL: See Flying Scale.

SEAPLANE: See Hydro Model.

SERVO: Motor-driven control surface actuator.

SHEET BALSA: Flat veneers of balsa usually 36 in. × 3 in.

S-HOOK: Wire fitting bent in the shape of an S connecting rubber motor to propeller shaft.

SIDE THRUST: Propeller shaft offset when viewed from above.

SIGNAL: Radio command emitted by transmitter.

SLABSIDE: Flat-sided fuselage construction.

S.M.A.E.: Society of Model Aeronautical Engineers. Body delegated by Royal Aero Club to administer aeromodelling in Great Britain.

SPACER: Length of wood spreading between major components.

GLOSSARY

SPAN: Length from tip to tip of a lifting surface.

SPAR: Spanwise load-carrying wing structural member.

SPIRAL STABILITY: Ability to turn in natural bank without tendency to spiral dive.

SPONSON: Stub wings added to hull on hydro model for lateral stability on water.

STABILITY: Ability of an airframe to return to normal flight after disturbance.

STALL: Loss of lift resulting from excess angle of attack.

STEP: Break in hydro model hull undersurface, to permit take-off water.

STRETCH WIND: Stretching of rubber motor to ease winding and ensure maximum number of turns.

SWEEP BACK: Angling back of a lifting surface relative to lateral datum.

TAB: Small control surface used for trimming.

TAIL: Lifting surfaces at rear of fuselage.

TAILLESS: Model designed with special airfoil or sweep back to eliminate tail surfaces.

TAILSKID: Wire, or wood protection for rear fuselage during landing and take-off.

TEAM RACING: Two or more models flying simultaneously in the same circuit.

TEMPLATE: Pattern in metal or wood for cutting duplicate components.

TENSIONER: Means of maintaining tautness in rubber motor. (Mechanical or by pre-tensioning of motor.)

THERMAL: Rising current of relatively warm air.

THINNERS: Solvents for paints, dopes used to reduce consistency.

THRUST: Propulsive power force obtained by propeller, jet or function of gravity.

THRUST LINE: Angle of propeller shaft relative to datum.

TIMER: Means of determining component action, for example, engine stop or dethermalizer.

TIP TAIL: Dethermalizer action of tailplane, raising trailing edge 35 deg.

TORQUE: Reactive force generated by revolving propeller or similar component.

TOW HOOK: Attachment for towing line on glider.

TOW LINE: Launching line for glider normally 50 metres long of nylon fishline.

GLOSSARY

TRACTOR: A pulling airscrew.

TRAILING EDGE: Extreme rear edge of lifting surface.

TRANSISTOR: Electronic means of gaining in efficiency or power.

TRANSMITTER: Radio control apparatus for emission of radio control signals.

TRICYCLE: Landing gear with three wheels.

TRIM: Adjustment for flight or decorative scheme.

T SPAR: Mainspar constructed with letter T cross section.

TUNED REED: Means of discriminating audio signals in radio control.

TUNGSTEN: Very thin diameter wire used for bracing indoor models.

TUNING: Reworking of miniature engines for increased performance.

TWIN FIN: Model having duplicate vertical tail surfaces.

TWO-STROKE: Internal combustion engine which fires on every other stroke of piston.

U CONTROL: Original American term for control-line flight.

UNDER CAMBER: Concave shape of aerofoil section, on bottom surface.

UNDERCARRIAGE: Landing gear.

UPTHRUST: Upward inclination of propeller shaft relative to datum.

VALVE: Gas-filled tube detector in a radio circuit.

VENEER: One laminate in a plywood section.

VENTURI: Aerodynamic means of inducing low pressure point in a carburettor.

VORTICE: Swirling airstream created by tips of surfaces, etc.

WAKEFIELD: International class contest rubber model named after Lord Wakefield, donor of original trophy.

WASH-IN: Aerodynamic twist in a wing lifting leading edge towards tips.

WASH-OUT: Aerodynamic twist in a wing lifting trailing edge towards tips.

WATER SHRINKING: Spraying of water on fabric or paper surface to shrink covering.

WAVE BAND: Frequency of radio transmission.

WINCH: Geared drum for winding glider tow line.

WINDER: Means of geared winding of rubber motors.

WING: Principal lifting surface.

WING SECTION: The aerofoil or rib shape.

Index

INDEX

Fuel proofer, 126
Fuselages, 110

Galloping Ghost, 82
Glass fibre, 28, 113
Glow plug, 43
Grain filler, 125
Grasses, 25
Graupner kits, 52

Hardwood, 25, 64
Helicopters, 101
Hourglass figure, 105

Incidence, angle of, 54
Indoor models, 17
Industrial models, 21
Internal combustion, 43
Inverted flight, 69

Japanese tissue, 31, 121, 128
Jetex, 48
Jets, 48
Jigs, 139, 141
Joints, 117

Knife, 35
Knock-off attachments, 64

Lateral stability, 57
Lead acid cells, 52
Licence (radio), 20
Lime, 25
Longitudinal stability, 54
Loops, 69
Lubricants, 42

Magnalux, 52
Magneto, 47
McCutcheon helicopter, 102
McMurdo Instruments Ltd., 52
Melinex, 127
Methanol, 44
Microfilm, 13, 31, 127, 128
Micromax motor, 52
Monoline, 72
Monowheel, 75
Moulding canopies, 131

National Championships, 104
Nitrate, 46
Nitro, 45, 137
Nylon, 31, 123, 124

Obechi, 25
Offset, 47, 60
Ornithopters, 96

Pantograph, 91
Penaud, 11, 39
Pen Bladder, 73
Pendulums, 56, 93, 94
Photostats, 91
Piano Wire, 34
Pins, 36
Plan enlargement, 91
Planking, 112
Plastics, 26, 100, 113, 114, 131
Pliers, 35
Plywood, 29
Priming, 45
Propellers, 47, 130, 136
Proportional control, 83
Proportional dividers, 91
P.V.A. glue, 30, 117, 127

Quadruplane, 98
Quarter grain, 23

Radio control, 20, 79
Rat Racing, 19, 77
Receivers, 79
Reed, 25
Reed bank, 80
Repairs, 139, 143
Research models, 21
Retractable undercarriage, 62, 82
Ribs, 115
Rotary porting, 47
Royalite, 26
Rubber drive, 17, 38
Rulag accumulator, 52

Sandwich ribs, 115
Scale models, 88, 106
Scrambles, 107
Sealers, 32, 119

159

INDEX

GW00360393

SUFFERING
A Biblical Perspective On Life's Greatest Puzzle

AMBASSADOR

INTRODUCTION

No greater challenge arises to faith than when, suddenly, trauma and heartache surge into a person's life. Suffering can come in many forms; it can come in the form of a broken love affair, an unhappy marriage, a business collapse or sudden unemployment. Perhaps its most traumatic form is when a child or teenager dies in a family and a parent lifts a weary head and asks that searing, burning question; "How could a loving God let this happen?"

Doubt, depression and loneliness often follow suffering and the sometimes inexplicable silence of God in it all can be most unsettling. People begin to feel that either God is not good or not Almighty, or begin to wonder if He is there at all. In our world of starving millions, terrorist outrages, and wars by the hundred, suffering people right across the earth cry for some meaning to the bizarre things happening all around them.

Is there a Biblical perspective on life's greatest puzzle?

Is there a clear-cut answer to suffering?

Let's investigate.

Derick Bingham

1. THE TOUR OF ALL TOURS

It is important to remember, right at the beginning of our investigation, that pain is essential to normal life on this planet. The pain network in our bodies has some remarkable features. For example: Without pain warnings, most sports would be too risky. Without pain, art and culture would be very limited. Without pain, our lives would be in mortal danger.

Those rare people who feel no pain have no warning of a ruptured appendics, heart attack or brain tumour. Without pain, musicians would have real problems. A guitarist, for example, must be able to feel exactly where his finger lands on the string and how hard it presses. Musicians rely on the body's sensitivity to pain and pressure. Without pain, there would be no sex, for sexual pleasure is mostly carried by pain cells. Pain is not something God thought up at the last moment to make our lives miserable. The millions of pain sensors in our bodies show God's intricate care for us. 1

Human suffering, though, involves more than pain. The Bible doesn't shrink from this fact, it steams right into it with the story of a man called Job. A whole book in the Bible is given to his story, a book of forty-two chapters. It is probably the oldest book in the world and the oldest statement of the never ending problem of human suffering.

At the outset, Job is placed before us as the model of a perfect man, the very paragon of his age. Rich and prosperous, he has seven sons and three daughters and is enjoying a very happy family life. He has a vast estate and immense possessions and seems to fit the popular equasion that personal goodness plus happy outward conditions equals the normal result of the righteous rule of God.

Suddenly, in one single day, Job, through a series of disasters and catastrophies, is deprived of his flocks and herds, his faithful servants and his loving children. As if such losses were not enough for any human to bear, his health breaks down and a horrible skin disease covers his entire body. The sore, angry swellings cause Job long and restless nights and as he is no longer able to work, he goes and sits down "Among the ashes" (Job 2;8). In all villages and cities of the east, the local rubbish dump was burned once a month and the ashes remained. If the city or village had been inhabited for a century, the rubbish dump known as the mezbele, reached quite a height. It gradually turned into a firm round mound of earth and served the inhabitants of the district as a watch tower and on close oppressive evenings as a place of assembly because there is a current of air on the height. There the children would play all day long and there the forsaken lay, by day asking alms of the passersby and at night hiding among the ashes which the sun had warmed.

Our investigation of human suffering leads us, then, to this poor man, bereaved, humiliated and in pain, sitting in a rubbish dump. His skin is festering, his nerves are on fire. Does the Bible present him sitting with a "stiff upper lip", unmoved by it all? Certainly not. He curses the very day he was born. (See Job 3; 1). Few people in history have described as graphically as Job how very wretched human existence can be. He declares that it would have been better never to have existed at all. He even curses the night of his conception and says "May it not be included among the days of the year". (Job 3; 6). He longs for death (Job 3; 11-19) and it seems the sole good left to him. Let no-one ever say that the Bible isn't realistic. Like millions of human beings after him, Job found life intolerable and death desirable, even a relief. Millions can identify with Job's words when he said; "Oh that my grief were fully weighed, and my calamity laid out in the balances, for then it would be heavier than the sand on the sea .... for the arrows of the Almighty are within me; my spirit drinks in their poison" (Job 6; 2-4). Job couldn't relax, he couldn't settle or rest, he was highly agitated and accused God of firing arrows at him.

In all of this the most surprising element is that God does not berate Job. God lets him pour out his grief and frustration and sorrow. He doesn't even interrupt him. Job's friends, though, have plenty to say and their interruptions are frequent.

They have a doctrine that says that God is good to the good and bad to the bad, and they rub it in to poor Job. They claim that Job must have sinned, else he wouldn't be suffering. "All his days the wicked man suffers torment", says Eliphaz (Job 15: 20). "The lamp of the wicked is snuffed out", adds Bildad (Job 18: 5) and to cap it all, Sophar says "The mirth of the wicked is brief" (Job 20:5). "Is not your wickedness great", they conclude, "Are not your sins endless?". (Job 22:5).

The interesting thing is that God does not accept the spiritual diagnosis of Job's three friends. He condemns what they have said as folly. (Job 42; 7-8). From this we learn in our investigation of human suffering, that God does not always use pain or suffering as a punishment. That He has done is shown in the history of the children of Israel but in every case, the punishment that they got follows repeated warnings against the behaviour that merits the punishment. Even the AIDS epidemic of our day is not without warning in Scripture. (Romans 1; 26-27). The prophets in Israel's day consistently warned of the dire consequences of Israel's behaviour.

Our friend Job, though, was not suffering as a result of wrongdoing any more than the blind man that Jesus spoke of in John 9; 1-5.

Why then did Job suffer? Job never found out in this life, yet, millions of us who

7

read the book of Job can now see that his suffering was the testing ground of a proposition put by Satan to God which, simply summed-up, asks, "Is a person capable of loving God even though there is no evident proof of God's love in their life and even though they don't, in this life, gain by loving God, but lose?". In other words, can God inspire affection in human beings, even though He does not appear to be affectionate? Until Christ came, the fact is that no individual soul ever made such a battle ground between God's power and the Devil's power as Job's soul did.

Job couldn't hide his despair with himself and with what God was allowing to happen to him, but, Job stuck to the point day and night that God is righteous and has a purpose, although everything in his actual experience seemed to prove the very opposite. In the midst of it all, Job's incredible leap of faith has since sent waves of courage to all suffering souls. The Bible tells us that his pain was so great that he "Took his flesh in his teeth", i.e. Job was in such misery he even bit his own flesh to ease the pain (Job 13; 14). Superbly, in the midst of his great personal suffering, Job suddenly makes one of the greatest statements of faith in all history; "Though He slay me, yet will I trust Him", he says (Job 13; 15).

What was God's answer to all that Job suffered? Did God say that He had power but not enough power to solve human suffering? Did He say that the mess this world was in was too much for Him? No, he took Job for a tour of tours and showed Him his creative genius. Job learned, in spite of his personal suffering, to trust God again because he was overwhelmed by the display of God's power in creation. Of course, the critics have poured scorn on God's response to Job's sufferings. George Bernard Shaw in "The Adventures of the Black Girl in Her Search for God" has her call the Lord's speech "A sneer". It is far from a sneer. God invites Job to meet him like a man (Job 38; 3) and never hints that it is not for him to question the ways of the Almighty. "The aim", one writer comments, "is not to crush Job. On the contrary, the mere fact that God converses with him gives him a dignity above all the birds and beasts, assuring him that it is a splendid thing to be a man. To look at any bird or flower is a revelation of God in His constant care for His world. Here is the proof that a person can love God for simply being God, not for reward. Here the lack of a formal answer to a moral question, indeed the narrowing of the spotlight of the book to one individual, is positively instructive."

What a tour God gives Job! In Chapter 38 of Job we read of God discussing the origin of the sea (v. 8-11), here is the miracle of the daily appearance of the day (v.

8

12-15), here is the vast subterranean region (v. 16-18). Here are the treasures of the snow (verse 22-23) or the rainstorm (v. 24-27). God shows Job the dew and ice and hoar frost and the great constellations of Pleiadaes and Orion (verse 28-33). God even teaches Job that no person can fully understand the movements of clouds (v. 34-38).

God then moves to things that are closer to Job. Man has been placed in charge of the world and yet no-one can "Hunt the prey for the lion or satisfy the appetite for the young lions". Yet, God is the primary cause for doing that very thing. Even the ravens are fed by Him (v. 39-41).

The tour continues as God displays to Job his intricate knowledge of the Ibex goat and his supervision of the breeding of their flocks. Instinct in animals is God's creation (39;1-4). The wild ass is wild because God made him wild (39; 1,5,16). The extinct Aurochs, (extinct since 1627) the most powerful of all hoofed beasts is discussed (39; 9-12) and even the ridiculousness of the ostrich is discussed in humorous detail (39; 13-18). The horse was never more perfectly described (39; 19-25) and the hawk and the eagle are pin- pointed (39;26-30).

To all of this and more, on the tour, Job's response is to worship God and trust Him again.

Job never gets to what really lies behind all his suffering, but he sees God in such a way that he doesn't need to. He trusts the God of creation and even though his suffering, bereavement and pain continue, he moves from asserting and defending himself to surrendering to God. The test Satan set would only work if Job did not know what the test was for. That is why it worked because Job never discovered what his suffering was about during his lifetime. Even though God's purpose in the details of Job's suffering life were not clear to Job, that did not stop him from trusting God and from crying out in the midst of his pain, "For I know that my Redeemer lives and He shall stand at last on the earth; and after my skin is destroyed, this I know, that in my flesh I shall see God, whom I shall see for myself, and my eyes shall behold, and not another". (Job 19; 25-27). What have we learned, then, from the story of Job about suffering?

We have learned:-
1. Personal suffering is not necessarily a result of personal sin.
2. Suffering can be the testing ground of the fact that a person can have affection for God even though God does not appear to be affectionate.

3. Suffering is not the proof that God is not all powerful.
4. Suffering raises great dilemmas and questions and it is certainly not a sin to ask questions to God when overwhelmed with difficult circumstances. God can and eventually will answer all our questions.
5. Suffering may surround us but we can learn to trust God again through an insight into His creative genius.
6. Suffering may give no clue to what God is up to in our personal circumstances but that is no reason for refusing to worship Him. We must allow God to know some things we don't.

Recently, while visiting Oxford University for the preaching of God's Word, I took a tour of the city on an open topped bus. My mind went back to that famous day in 1929 when the atheistic C. S. Lewis was going up Headington Hill in Oxford on the top of a bus when he became aware that he was holding God "At bay". He writes, "Amiable agnostics will talk cheerfully about 'Man's search for God'. To me, as I then was, they might as well have talked about the mouse's search for the cat!". Later that evening the result of the long conviction of his mind and heart by the Holy Spirit came to a head and Lewis asks us to picture him alone in his room at Magdalen College. "Night after night, feeling, whenever my mind lifted even for a second from my work, the steady, unrelenting approach of Him whom I so earnestly desired not to meet. That which I greatly feared had at last come upon me. In the Trinity Term of 1929, I gave in, and admitted that God was God, and knelt and prayed: perhaps that night the most dejected and reluctant convert in all England. I did not then see what is now the most shining and obvious thing; the Divine humility which will accept a convert even on such terms.

The Prodigal Son at least walked home on his own feet. But who can duly adore that Love which will open the high gates to a prodigal who is brought in kicking, struggling, resentful, and darting his eyes in every direction for a chance of escape?

The words "compelle intrare", compel them to come in, have been so abused by wicked men that we shudder at them; but properly understood, they plumb the depths of the Divine mercy. The hardness of God is kinder than the softness of men, and His compulsion is our liberation."[2]

If C. S. Lewis was a reluctant convert, he became an outstanding believer. So it was that though Job questioned and accused, raged and rampaged about the meaning of life and the horror of suffering, he certainly became one of the most outstanding believers in history. With Oswald Chambers I want to say, "Next to Jesus, Job must surely be the greatest believer in the whole Bible". Let's move on, then, to investigate suffering in the life of the Lord Jesus.

2. GOD IN PAIN

W hen Stephen Speilberg produced his Box Office hit film E.T., millions were moved to weep when they saw it. Speilberg said the film was his "Cry to the stars for a friend". As most science fiction stories make all alien characters a threat to our existence, Speilberg decided to create a character who would come to love us. In the film the character Extra Terrestrial was found by an American boy in the backyard of his own home.

When we think of millions of people weeping at a Holywood fantasy, the tragedy is that the story of the Gospel, which is in every respect true, seems to move so few. God, incarnate, was literally found in the back yard of an inn by some shepherds during the reign of Caesar Augustus at the height of the Roman Empire. Here was no alien creature come to love us, here was God of very God wrapped in swaddling clothes and lying in a manger. "There was no beauty that we should desire Him", said the prophet Isaiah of the event, long before it happened. In other words, Christ had no halo of light around His head, He smiled and cried and had to be fed and was dependent on His mother and had to learn to talk like any other child.

The incarnation of God has very wonderful lessons to teach us about the whole question of human suffering. God does not address us from the clouds, or from a pulpit, or through a tract on the street, but to reach us He becomes one of us and to do that involved suffering like us.

Did He suffer? No-one ever suffered like He did. He was called a Man of Sorrows. In Hebrew the word for "sorrows" is "kaab" meaning "to be in pain". So, literally, Christ was a "Man of Pains".

From the very beginning of His earthly life to His death, He was surrounded by pain of all kinds, both external and internal, both physical and psychological. The legitimacy of His birth was doubted. His family, when He began His earthly ministry, thought He was out of His mind. When His own home town crowd heard about His actions they said, "He has lost His senses". The Scribes concluded that He was in league with the Devil and said so. He was betrayed by one of His closest friends, faced false charges, was tried by a prejudiced jury and convicted by a cowardly judge. He was tortured. He was then taken out and crucified, forsaken by His disciples, His nation and finally by God the Father. He was indeed a Man of Sorrows.

"Where do broken hearts go?", Whitney Houston used to sing. We answer that they had best go to Gethsemane and Calvary for they will find a sympathy there which is not to be found anywhere else. It is a very profound experience for all suffering people to meditate upon the pain that Christ suffered in His last hours.

It is sacred ground and as we now approach it, we shall have to tread softly as we look on our suffering Lord, the "Lifter-up of our heads".

We come first across the Kedron valley and begin to climb the Mount of Olives and turn off into an olive orchard known as Gethsemane. Christ had often met there with His disciples but this time something happens which the world has never seen, before or since. It cries out for an explanation and pulls back the curtain on what the cross meant to the Saviour. We are told that He went forward alone by Himself to pray and was "Overwhelmed with sorrow to the point of death". Frightening terms are employed by the Gospels to describe Christ's mental anguish. Loathing, aversion, appalled reluctance, alarmed dismay, and consternation are part of the original language used to describe His suffering at this point.

The Saviour's reluctance to drink the bitter cup before Him was not because He was reluctant to face death or because He was afraid His friends would desert Him. It was not even fear of His enemies that overwhelmed Him. Charles II for example faced execution fearlessly. Was England's King braver than the Son of God? No. The fact remains that in that cup the Saviour had to drink was the divine punishment Christ had to bear when He was to "Bear our sins in His own body on the tree". So great was His anguish that His sweat was like drops of blood falling to the ground. Truly, if the anticipation of the cross was so tormenting, what must the real thing have been like?

Soon He was betrayed and roughly treated like a common criminal and taken away by soldiers from Gethsemane. He was spitten upon, beaten and bound. A crown of thorns was placed on His sacred head and He was mocked. They drove spikes into His hands and feet and when He was hung on the cross, darkness was all over the land from twelve noon to three p.m. It was an outward symbol of the spiritual darkness which enveloped Him. He came out of that darkness crying "My God, my God, why have You forsaken Me?" Sadly, Lloyd Webber and Rice in their rock opera "Jesus Christ Superstar" take this statement to signify that Christ was doubting His mission and make the cross out to be a good plan gone all wrong. Millions of people have been influenced by this thinking and believe it to be the truth. It was no such thing. Christ's death was no mistake but rather a Divine atonement for our sins. He came to die and His orphan cry on the cross was a quotation from Psalm 22, verse 1; "My God, my God, why have You forsaken Me?". The very same Psalm answers the question by giving the reason for the Father's abandonment of the Son on the cross. It states, "You are Holy" (Psalm 22; 4). The Father forsook His Son in those dreadfully dark hours because of His holiness. "For He made Him who knew no sin to be sin for us, that we might become the righteousness of God in Him" (2 Corinthians 4; 21).

He was utterly alone and bore the penalty we deserved and when it was through He gave the most challenging cry in all the Scriptures; "Teletestai", which in the perfect tense means "it has been and will for ever remain finished". No work was ever more perfect.

Are you suffering? Are you beside yourself with shame or despair? Are you weary? Stand by the cross with the blind and personally suffering George Mathison and say,

"O cross that liftest up my head, I dare not ask to fly from Thee, I lay in dust life's glory dead, And from the ground there blossoms red, Life that shall endless be". There is no telling whose eye might fall on this little book and, burdened one, I call you to meditate for a moment on the following priceless texts. They come from One who knows what you are going through more than anyone ever can.

"Come to me, all you labour and are heavy laden, and I will give you rest. Take my yoke upon you and learn from Me, for I am gently and lowly in heart, and you will find rest for your souls. For My yoke is easy and my burden is light". (Matthew 11;28-29).

"There is therefore now no condemnation to those who are in Christ Jesus, who do not walk according to the flesh, but according to the Spirit. For the law of the Spirit of life in Christ Jesus has made me free from the law of sin and death". (Romans 8; 1-2).

"Who shall bring a charge against God's elect? It is God who justifies. Who is He who condemns? It is Christ who died, and furthermore is also risen, who is even at the right hand of God, who also makes intercession for us. Who shall separate us from the love Christ? Shall tribulation, or distress, or persecution, or famine, or nakedness, or peril, or sword? .... For I am persuaded that neither death nor life, nor angels nor principalities nor powers, nor things present nor things to come, nor height nor depth, nor any other created thing, shall be able to separate us from the love of God which is in Christ Jesus our Lord". (Romans 8; 33-35, 38-39).

As we think of the cross, it is very important, then, that we ask what the relationship is between Christ's pain and ours. Here are six very helpful links:

1. The cross of Christ is a stimulus to patient endurance.
   (Hebrews 12; 1-3).
2. The cross of Christ is the path to mature holiness. (Hebrews 5; 8-9),

i.e. Christ's sufferings were the testing ground in which His obedience became full grown or mature.

3. The cross of Christ is the symbol of suffering service. (John 12; 23-26: Ephesians 3; 1-13: Colossians 1; 24: 2 Timothy 2; 8-10).

4. The cross of Christ is the hope of final glory. i.e. The hope of glory makes suffering bearable. (Romans 8; 28).

5. The cross of Christ is the ground of reasonable faith. (Romans 8; 32).

6. The cross of Christ is the proof of God's solitary love. (John 3; 16). 3

It is true that suffering is part of life, and suffering is an alien intrusion into God's good world and will have no place or part in the new Heaven and the new Earth. It is also true that we can bring suffering on ourselves. When we neglect or abuse or bodies, we will suffer the consequences. Cirrhosis of the liver can come through the drinking of alcohol. A reckless driver may break his neck. We have no right to hold it against God if we suffer a consequence of our foolish choices. Yet, sin apart, God has joined us in our suffering and the cross of Christ certainly calls us to trust Christ as Saviour and pin our hope in a God who is constantly working out a purpose. I shall never forget approaching a friend of mine, badly injured in his eye by a terrorist bomb, to seek to comfort him. He turned to me gently and said; "If God can bring order out of the chaos of the cross, He can bring order out of the chaos of my face". Despite all the problems surrounding the question of suffering, one thing is clear; Philip Yancey has put it this way: "Consistently the Bible directs the issue away from a question of cause to a question of response". "Is God fair?" we ask in the midst of our pain. "I am in control, no matter how it looks" is God's only answer. And, then, He has a question for us, one question; "Do you trust Me?". When I see the cross, I say, yes. Do you?

3. SUFFERING CAN BE PRODUCTIVE

In the former chapter we have seen that the Lord Jesus demonstrated that blessing comes through suffering and I now want to show from Scripture and from life the irreputable fact that there are a cloud of witnesses that prove this principle to be true. I want to show that it is as important "what" we get out of suffering as "that" we get out of it. Scripture shows that all believers are "Training for reigning". For example, through Paul's First Letter to the Corinthians we see that the church at Corinth was going through a rough patch with all kinds of differences rising between believers. They were threatening to take each other to the public court and Paul pleads with them not to do so. He argues that it is vital they sort out their problems within their local church, because, he says, "Do you not know that the saints will judge the world? And if the world will be judged by you, are you unworthy to judge the smallest matters? Do you not know that we shall judge angels? How much more, things that pertain to this life".

In other words, if they didn't have any training in how to make moral decisions during their lifetime, how could they one day judge the world and angels in the New Heaven and the New Earth? All kinds of administration will have to be carried out in the coming kingdom and the pressures and problems and heartaches that christians know here on earth can be turned round to train them for serving Christ in a coming day. So it has been that God has always used suffering to teach His people lessons so that they might serve Him better, not only in this life, but in the life that is to come. They are put through testing so that they might "Come forth as gold" (Job 23; 1O). "Don't reject the place of your prostration", said George Matheson, "It has ever been your robing-room for royalty. Ask the great ones of the past what has been the spot of their prosperity: they will say, 'It was the cold ground on which I was lying' ". Let's then ask a few great ones if this principle is true. Let's call them as witnesses.

Let's start with Abraham. Who could begin to describe the pressure Abraham felt as he climbed Mount Moriah? God had promised Abraham that through his son Isaac, all the world is going to be blessed. For long years Abraham has trusted God for the birth of Isaac and, through a miracle, Isaac came. Now God is about to test Abraham's faith by asking that he sacrifice his son. How could God keep his word and let Isaac die? How could the childless Isaac die and the promise still stand of a nation to be founded through him that would be as innumerable as stars and sand?

Scripture later tells us how Abraham got through this time of suffering that tested his faith. We read that he accounted "That God was able to raise him up, even from the dead" (Hebrews 11; 19). He believed that God was perfectly capable of resurrecting the body of Isaac.

It is no easy journey that Abraham makes up Mount Moriah and what parent could not identify with the heart-wrenching question of Isaac as he asks, "My father .... behold the fire and the wood; but where is the lamb for a burnt offering?" Yet,

Abraham's faith held; he calculated on God's being able to supply all his need. God's stores of supply are inexhaustible and as the very blade of Abraham's knife flashes in the rays of the sun, the voice of an angel from Heaven cries, "Do not lay your hand on the lad or do anything to him; for now I know that you fear God since you have not withheld your son, your only son, from me".

What did Abraham call the name of the place of his testing? He called it "Jehovah-jireh" meaning "The Lord will provide". Abraham finds a ram caught by his horns in a thicket and as it is sacrified in the place of Isaac, he is taught the great doctrine of substitution. As he leaves the mountain brow of his suffering, Abraham hears the voice of God; "By myself I have sworn, says the Lord, because you have done this thing, and have not withheld your son, your only son, in blessing I will bless you, and in multiplying I will multiply your descendents as the stars of the heaven and as the sand which is on the seashore; and your descendents shall possess the gates of their enemy.

In your seed all the nations of the earth shall be blessed, because you have obeyed my voice" (Genesis 22; 16-18). Ask Abraham and he would tell you that suffering can be very productive.

Let's try another. Let's ask Joseph if the truth of blessings coming through buffetings is true. Let's break into his story when his father Jacob sends the seventeen year old Joseph to Schechem to find out how his brothers are. Little did Jacob think that as Joseph left him to go to Shechem, he would not see his son again for twenty-two years. Poor Joseph! The Scripture speaks of a man finding Joseph wandering in a field at Shechem. Can you see him there in that field, unable to find his brothers and maybe, in his heart, wishing he wouldn't. Enthusiasm is always easier than obedience but Joseph obeys his father. Obedience, though it brought Joseph much suffering, actually eventually brought incalculable reward.

Joseph eventually found his brothers who immediately wanted to kill him. By the intervention of his brother, Reuben, Joseph is put in a pit. As Joseph lies in the pit do you think he shouts, "Praise the Lord, don't you fellows know I am to be governor of Egypt and am going to free you one day from death and starvation? This pit is marvellous because it is the actual highway of God's guidance for me!"? I am quite sure Joseph thought no such thing. He thought he was merely doing his duty and I am sure, wondered why on earth he was suffering for it. In fact he made a strong protest against the treatment he was receiving (see Genesis 42: 21).

No part of any suffering in our lives appears to be the path to blessing. Joseph in the pit looks broken beyond repairing. Gone is the coat of distinction, gone is home support, gone is every visible means of hope. But God has a purpose in it all; God does not bring good out of evil but He does bring good in spite of evil. All things that happen to us are not necessarily good, but they work together for good; His promise can be trusted. If God wants you out of where you are, He will take you out. You don't need to know key people, you just need to know the one who holds the keys. God can use just whatever He chooses to accomplish His will for you. A stalled sun for Joshua. A fleece for Gideon. A jawbone for Samson. A floating axe-head for Elisha. A lump of figs for Hezekiah. A raised golden sceptre for Esther. A burning coal for Isaiah. A great fish for Jonah. A coin in a fish's mouth for Peter. A blinding light for Paul.

The pit for Joseph was God's highway to saving a nation and preserving the line for the Messiah. Joseph goes on to bear his suffering with great dignity via the prison house and on to the governership of Egypt.]He showed sterling qualities under all the pressure. Here is ability without instability. Here is attractiveness without vanity. Here is cheerfulness without lightness. Here is gift without lording.]Here is courage without rough handling. Here is godliness that is as real to the man as breathing. Here is someone who did not wait for some great occasion but who made every occasion great. Suffering is very productive in Joseph's life.

My next witness is Moses; he didn't even have to wait for suffering to begin in his teenage years. Moses' suffering lay around him in his infancy. What is that ark of bulrushes floating in the Nile? It contains the little baby Moses hidden from the murderous edict of Pharoah who wanted every male Hebrew infant slain. If you had talked to the mighty Moses of later years, he would have dated his fortune from his danger in the Nile that day. Pharoah's daughter, accompanied by a team of maidens, comes down to the bank of the river to bathe and seeing the ark sends her maid to get it . Now, mark this. When Pharoah's daughter opened the lid of the ark, she saw the baby Moses and, we are told, "The babe wept, so she had compassion on him". The entire destiny of a nation hung on that little baby's tears!

Those tears moved a heart to bring up Moses in Pharoah's palace and led the way to the most famous exodus in history. Suffering was certainly an intrusion into the lives of the Hebrew people, but it led to great blessing.

My next witness is Ruth. If you and I had happened, by chance, to come walking past two women called Ruth and Naomi standing by the border of Moab and Israel, we would probably have walked on. Just two women talking by the side of the road, the wind blowing up dust as usual, the sun pouring down on the quiet countryside at the time of barley harvest. Yet, things are never as they seem. In the heart of Ruth there struggled the biggest decision in her young life. Recently widowed, she was deciding to leave Moab to help her mother-in-law who was returning, after much suffering in her life, to Bethlehem, in Israel. Ruth had discovered the true God and was she going back to the worldly substitutes in Moab that never satisfy? Before her lies the loneliness of an alien land, the hard back-breaking work of a gleaner and a future that seems terribly blank.

Ruth made a very clear decision and declares to her mother-in-law, "Your God shall be my God". Though it meant much personal suffering, Ruth went to Bethlehem and became King David's great-grandmother. From her family line came the Saviour of the world. She may have seemed peculiar to her friends but better a thousand times effective peculiarity than uneffective ordinariness. Her complete subordination to a single aim was absolute. The end, though, lay far from gleaning alien corn. It meant an eternal spiritual harvest.

The end, as Amy Carmichael wrote, it will explain;

> "Will not the end explain
> The crossed endeavour, earnest purpose foiled.
> The strange bewilderment of good work spoiled,
> The clinging weariness, the inward strain,
> Will not the end explain?

> Meanwhile He comforteth
> Them that are losing patience. 'Tis His way:
> But none can write the words they hear Him say
> For men to read; only they know He saith
> Sweet words and comforteth.

> Not that He doth explain
> The mystery that baffleth; but a sense
> Husheth the quiet heart, that far, far hence
> Lieth a field set thick with golden grain
> Wetted in seedling days by many a rain:
> The end - it will explain."

My final Bible witness is a New Testament couple. They were called Aquila and Priscilla. This christian couple, tentmakers by trade, were absolutely devoted to one another. Here were a couple who had everything going for them: they were living in Rome and rich in love. But, suddenly, the clouds began to gather on the horizon of their happiness. There were riots in the streets of the Jewish colony across the Tiber and the cause was that old chestnut of Jewish discord, "Who was the Messiah?".

Aquila, who was a Jew, and his wife remained faithful to Christ but, along with many others, faced fanatical opposition. Whispers began to pass around the imperial court that there was a seditious movement about. "Another king, one Jesus". So it was not very difficult for the Emperor to issue a short Act ordering the immediate deportation of all Jews.

For Aquila and Priscilla it meant financial disaster because every Roman soldier carried a tent on his back when on a campaign, and Rome was the great centre for the Roman army. Some of the Jews evaded the order and hid in the slums, but Aquila and Priscilla were loyal to the order of their earthly Sovereign and moved to Corinth.

Perhaps there is someone reading this little book who has been forced to move from their town, village or city to another place. You think God has forgotten you. It is not so. Let the example of God's dealings with this couple be a starlight of encouragement to you.

Aquila and Priscilla were not only devoted to each other, they were also devoted to the servants of Christ. After they had been in Corinth for some time, Paul came to the city. He was lonely and his Athenian mission had been less promising than he had hoped. He was not well supplied with funds and the finger of God's providence led him to Aquila and Priscilla's place of business for he, like them, was a tentmaker by trade. There grew up between this trio a loyal devotion to one another which made a deep impression on Paul's mind (See Romans 16; 4). For eighteen months, life passed busily and then they moved, under the call of God, to Ephesus. Here, Priscilla and Aquila earned more money and had a large business - room consecrated for christian worship, because there were no public places of worship for christians.

It was here the Ephesian christians gathered, here that Timothy learned more of Christ and here that Apollos, the great scholar and orator from Alexandria was taught the Gospel by this godly couple, and Apollos became one of the greatest servants of Christ in New Testament days. (See Acts 18: 24-26).

Devoted to each other, and to the truth of God, Paul said of Aquila and Priscilla: "Not only I but all the churches of the Gentiles are grateful to them" (Romans 16: 3). What an inspiration they are to us today! Despite having to move their business because of a nasty government edict, and despite all the personal suffering that came to them as a result, Aquila and Priscilla were mightily used by God to be in the vanguard for the establishment of the New Testament church. Their suffering was so productive it was to influence millions.

Let's take a few witnesses from life in general.

Who, in history, composed our greatest symphonies? Beethoven, Handel, Schubert, Chopin, Schuman, Debussy, Tchaikovsky and Dvorak are amongst our greatest composers. A look at their lives is a very illuminating experience; a little research leaves the researcher gasping. Beethoven spent his youth in poverty and misery.

As he grew older he was generally referred to as an ugly man. Tragedy of tragedies for Beethoven, he went stone deaf. It was a terrible thing to happen to a musician, and yet it was after this that he wrote some of his most wonderful music - music which he never heard himself. He never stopped producing masterpieces; 9 symphonies, 32 piano sonatas, 17 string quartets amongst a list of other works. The last twelve years of his life were lonely and unhappy and after four months of intense suffering from lung inflammation he died in December 1827 in the midst of a thunderstorm.

Handel first had to play the clavichord in an attic in case his father discovered him! Later in life, after many adventures, he composed his most widely popular work "The Messiah" under a cloud of misfortune and bitter disappointment. His last two operas had failed, largely through the plots of opponents who even hired ruffians to prevent people reaching the building where the operas were being performed. Later in life Handel went blind but he refused to give in, playing from memory and giving sound to the endless and wonderful music passing through his mind.

Schubert was, they say, a physically squat, stout, clumsy little man with an unhealthy complexion and rounded shoulders. Yet, music simply poured out of him. Chopin was plagued with ill health all his life and he had to fight constantly against disease. In later years his life was one long struggle against consumption. It was said, "He came into the room bent double and with a distressing cough ... but when he sat down to the piano he played with extraordinary strength and animation." He died at the age of 39.

Ilich Tchaikovsky had moods that alternated between happy exhuberant spirits and black depression. (Who of us hasn't?) He married a girl whom he did not love because he was afraid she would commit suicide if he refused her. After nine weeks they separated and Tchaikovsky suffered such mental torture he became unconscious. Although he said he was "worn out" and "done for", he was conceiving in his mind the haunting and beautiful "Pathetique" Symphony. He unfortunately drank some unboiled water which brought about a fatal attack of cholera.

The story is no different in many other fields of worthy endeavour. The blind Milton wrote the classic "Paradise Lost". The childhood suffering of Charles Dickens produced "David Copperfield". Robert Louis Stevenson showed no trace of the boredom of an invalid's life in "Treasure Island". Livingstone opened Africa through unbelievable personal suffering.

What shall we say of the Pilgrim Fathers setting out to found the "New World"? Were there not many tears in the process? Yet, in all of these examples suffering was productive.

We have covered a fair bit of ground since we first set out to investigate the question of suffering from a Biblical standpoint. Does the Bible, then, give us a clear-cut answer to human suffering? I would have to say that I don't really think it gives us so much a clear-cut answer to suffering as i t gives us a clear-cut way to go through it. When Paul asked God three times to remove his "Thorn in the flesh", he was not told why he was suffering, but he was told by God that "My grace is sufficient for you and My strength is made perfect in weakness". It is here, then, that I rest my case. Though we may not always know why we suffer, we are promised liberating, thrilling, revolutionary, amazing, enabling grace to get us through our suffering, if we trust God through it all.

Another thing is also absolutely sure; incalculable blessing always lies at the end. "This present suffering", says the Bible, "is not to be compared with the glory that shall follow". I leave you with one final story. It could, maybe, only happen in Northern Ireland, but it certainly happened to me. I had been preaching God's

Word in South Korea and developed, while there, a huge swelling. I went, on returning home to Northern Ireland, to see a doctor friend of mine who is also a christian. "Are you worried?", he asked with a twinkle in his eye when I entered his surgery and explained my problem. "Worried!", I replied, "I am frightened out of my mind!". "Well, you are not going to die then," he said. "How's that?", I asked. "Because if you were going to die, you would get dying grace, wouldn't you? Since you obviously haven't got it, you're not going to die, yet!". I thought him somewhat comfortless at the time but after the last twenty years of life's experiences, I have found he spoke more comforting truth than I could have ever imagined.

REFERENCES

1. 'Where is God When it Hurts?' by Philip Yancey.
2. 'Surprised by Joy', C. S. Lewis, Inspirational Press, New York, p.125.
3. 'The Cross of Christ', J.R.W. Stott, Inter-Varsity Press, p.315-337.

Derick Bingham is a Bible teacher with the
Crescent Church, Belfast. The following is a selection of
message tapes from "Tuesday Night at the Crescent"

JOY - THE CHRISTIAN'S SECRET STRENGTH
A study of Paul's letter to the Philippians

Confidence: The basis of joy
Tough Circumstances: The test of joy
Consistency: The progress of joy
Christlikeness: The completion of joy
Self: The enemy of joy
Friends: The fellowship of joy
Pride: The killer of joy
Principle: The anchor of joy
Citizenship: The mark of joy
Harmony: The music of joy
Worry: The disturber of joy
Contentment: The fruit of joy
Power: The fuel of joy

HOME, WHERE LIFE MAKES UP ITS MIND

Is family life facing extinction?
What is God's blueprint for marriage?
Is monogamy God's will?
Is marriage God's plan for everyone?
The most unpopular requirement for marriage
Are we undertaking marriage too lightly?
Is marriage worth waiting for?
Why do couples fight?
Don't be a passive parent
How should we discipline our children?
Living with teenagers
When the unbearable is inescapable
Tell debt do us part
Commitment is the key

THE RELUCTANT HERO
A study of the life of Moses

Born after midnight
Lessons learned from failure
Burning bridges or bushes
Lord here am I, send Aaron!
When they all stand up against you
Plaques that preach
The night nobody slept
Between the devil and the deep Red Sea
Is the Lord testing you?
Giving up a good thing for a better
Reverence, the forgotten attitude
The believers occupational hazards
What bad temper can do
Do shadows frighten you

THERE IS AN ALTERNATIVE

Studies in the Sermon on the Mount

The most radical lifestyle, ever
The richest self-fulfilment possible
How to make life tasty
Overcoming anger and lust
Divorce and oathtaking: are they permissible?
Should we turn the other cheek?
How to love your enemy
Beware! Religious performance now showing
Are you into prayer and fasting
The tragedy of Mr Facing Bothways
Are you a worrier?
Putting an end to labelling people
The narrow way doesn't get broader
The simple secret of an unsinkable life
The amazing Lord Jesus

DOES GOD STILL GUIDE?

Biblical principles on knowing God's will for your life

Guidance: Why do we need it?
Guidance: When does it come?
Guidance: How do we know it?
Guidance: Can we stray from it?
Guidance: Does prayer affect it?
Guidance: Why is it often delayed?
Guidance: So, what about it?

THE ROAD LESS TRAVELLED BY

A study of Christ's influence in life's decisions

When you are facing temptation
When you are facing misunderstanding
When you are facing doubt
When you are facing inadequacy
When you are facing pain
When you are facing disqualification
When you are facing shame
When you are facing success addiction
When you are facing a need for grace